ISBN : 978-2-37301-059-6
EAN : 9782373010596
Éditions Jean-Pierre Otelli
www.editions-jpo.com
Tous droits de traduction, de reproduction
et d'adaptation réservés pour tous pays.
T : + 33 (0) 1 85 08 75 92
Maquette / Graphisme : Naoual Otelli
Révision : Valérie Eveillé - Caractère essentiel
© Éditions Jean-Pierre Otelli Mars 2017

Jean-Pierre Otelli

Pilot Errors
Volume 5

Translated from the French by
Alan McKay & Gerard Traynor

Éditions JPO

À ma mère, au ciel...

FOREWORD

This is the fifth volume in the Pilot Errors series; it will probably come in for a lot of criticism, possibly even more virulent than that received by earlier publications, especially since this one deals with the Rio-Paris flight...

I will be blamed for revealing information that is supposed to remain within the profession and these revelations will damage the inflated image many pilots have of themselves. Unfortunately, the facts speak for themselves and we are not as perfect as the general public would like to believe. Pilots are ordinary people with their individual qualities and failings. They all make mistakes (the author of these lines included). However, the best way to improve safety is to be truthful and come clean on such blunders so lessons can be learnt by other pilots and crew members.

The accidents described and analysed here were not chosen haphazardly. They all reveal surprising similarities, among which, in particular:

- Inexperienced crew members.
- Poorly trained First Officers.
- Captains in a state of stress or simply in too much of a hurry to get going.
- Tired, even exhausted, crews.
- Disproportionate reactions completely unrelated to the set procedures for the given situation.

None of the crashes analysed in this book would have occurred if one simple maxim, best summed up in a single word – *procedure* – had been respected. Flying an aircraft is above all about accurately performing the gestures that correspond to a given task or problem. Such gestures cannot be improvised. Their definition is the fruit of an enormous amount of work, a painstaking intellectual exercise involving the aircraft manufacturer, the airline and pilot training schools.

In the vast majority of cases, this system of procedures works normally and the level of safety remains satisfactory. Then from time to time a grain of sand gets into the works and things seize up. But there is always a reason - someone forgot a checklist or a pilot reacted without thinking; and from then on things start to get complicated...

PUSH YOUR SEAT BACK

26 May 2010

The aircraft in this story is a Boeing 737-800 belonging to Air India Express, Air India's low-cost subsidiary. Registered as VT-AXJ, it was practically brand new and the least that can be said of it is that it never went unnoticed on arriving at an airport for the art work on the tail is quite outstanding. This was due to the airline, AICL[1], deciding to set itself apart from its rivals by decorating its aircraft with stunning artistry with quite extraordinary results... The aircraft are so splendid that they are among the most photographed in the world. On internet forums, plane spotters even describe them as true works of art. Each aircraft sports a different motif. Some are decorated with animals (for example, a huge white tiger, a cobra or an elephant) while others show emblematic Indian sites, including the Taj Mahal, the Victoria Memorial or the Himalayas. The aircraft in this story sported an architectural motif taken from the Red Fort[2]. Everyone agrees it was a marvel of graphics.

The aircraft in this story (registration VT-AXJ)

---

[1] In advertising brochures, the airline uses the name Air India Express, but its real designation is Air India Charters Ltd. The initials used in the investigation report and in administrative documents are therefore AICL.
[2] A fortress built by Emperor Shah Jahan in the 17th century in the old town of Delhi and a huge tourist attraction.

It was night-time... That evening, the "Red Fort" Boeing was flying between Dubai and the town of Puna with 113 passengers on board. This was flight N° IX 212 that had taken off at 20.30 local time[3]. After take-off, the aircraft took heading 117 to the south-east and was cleared to climb directly to its cruising altitude.

Most of the passengers were male immigrant Indian workers largely employed in the building industry. Some of them were going home on holiday but most were leaving the Emirates for good following the economic crisis that had hit Dubai so putting paid to its grand construction projects.

The aircraft levelled off at Level 370[4] and was flying at Mach 0.76[5]. All was quiet aboard. Puna is 1,250 miles from Dubai and the estimated flight time was 2 hours 55 minutes. The weather was perfect and the night was peaceful over the northern Indian Ocean with no turbulence and not the slightest trace of cloud. As the whole trip was over water, all radio communication was by HF.

The Captain was 39 years old. He had just 6,000 flying hours behind him but he had a good reputation as a serious pilot and nothing untoward was reported in his professional file.

The First Officer was 25 and still had to obtain his airline pilot's licence although he held his CPL/IR[6]. Having logged just 1,310 flying hours, his professional experience was extremely limited. He was something of a beginner.

At that time, the airline seemed to be having trouble recruiting crews. Illustrative of this was the fact that when a passenger bought a ticket on the internet, they were also informed that the airline was seeking to recruit 40 Captains. This was rather an unusual intrusion since these job offers were actually posted on the very page where the customers booked their seats! All the necessary conditions were specified: required experience[7],

---

[3] To better understand the sequence of events, all times in this narrative are expressed in Dubai time, which is UTC +4 hours.

[4] 37,000 feet or 11,250 m.

[5] At high altitude, the speed of an aircraft is measured in relation to the speed of sound, Mach 1. In the present instance, the Boeing was flying at 76% of the speed of sound.

[6] Commercial Pilot's Licence with an Instrument Rating. This licence does not qualify the holder to be a Captain aboard a "multi-pilot" aircraft in public transport.

[7] The airline requires at least 2,000 hours (which is very little) of which 100 aboard Boeing 737-800s (also very little). The salary offered was also very low for the profession at roughly 8,000 Euros a month.

ideal qualifications, but also the salary offered and the age limit. Passengers also learned that the airline recruited up to the age of 56 but was willing to make exceptions. However, there was no minimum age for being taken on. The only other requirement was to be more than 5 feet tall. There cannot have been many applicants turned down for that reason!

You also learned that these job offers were only intended for Indian pilots but that they also took into account the caste system of social stratification. This meant that among the 40 Captains that Air India Charters Ltd wanted to recruit, there would be:
- 20 Captains from the General Class,
- 6 from the Scheduled Class ("untouchables"),
- 4 from the Scheduled Tribe ("aboriginals"),
- 10 from the Other Backward Communities.

Naturally this selection technique would be impossible in western society, but it is regarded as being perfectly acceptable in India, even being expressly recognised by the Constitution of India.

The first half of the trip went perfectly normally as the passengers tucked into the free although rather frugal meal offered on board, mainly consisting of rice, dhal (a spiced lentil dish) and naan bread all served without cutlery in home delivery pizza-like cartons. This service is greatly appreciated by many of the low paid workers who fly low-cost but also benefits the airline considerably and forms a major part of its communications strategy.

At **21:47**, the Boeing left the Muscat Zone and switched to HF radio communication under Mumbai control. It was a routine daily flight between the Emirates and India and all crews knew the route by heart. The aircraft was now following Airway N 571, a kind of air expressway which took it to Point "Parar". Regional control had just cleared it to continue on its route as on the flight plan and it was now heading to reporting Point "Doget".

It was **21:53** when events began to take a more unusual turn. The lighting in the cockpit had been turned up as much as possible; outside over the Indian Ocean it was pitch black.

Sitting on the right, the First Officer had pushed his seat right back so he could fill in the flight documents. In so doing, the seat became embedded well into the right hand corner of the cockpit[8].

---

[8] The runners the seat sits on are S-shaped meaning that when the seat is pushed back it is taken much closer to the partition. This gives the pilots room to leave their seats more easily.

Whatever their function aboard the aircraft, it is always the First Officer who does all the paperwork needed on the flight. On the left, the Captain had put down the microphone with which he had just contacted Mumbai control. He then called the Cabin Senior hostess over the interphone.
"I'm coming out … Can you come to the galley please."
The Cabin Senior confirmed that she had come along and the Captain put the receiver down[9].
After a few moments' silence, he unfastened his belt and spoke to the First Officer calmly:
"I'm going to the washroom, hold the fort, will you?"
The First Officer responded immediately:
"Yes, sir."
The Captain pushed his seat back and stepped over the central console. There is no regulation stating that they may not leave the cockpit. They can leave for a pressing need but also go and settle in the cabin and talk to the passengers or stretch their legs in the galley and remain absent for as long as they like. This is perfectly normal procedure. Naturally a Captain will never leave the cockpit during the critical take-off, landing and approach phases. But for all the other flight phases, you have to trust their sense of responsibility. Some airlines simply require the pilot to stay at the controls to take certain precautions. In general, the procedure requires the remaining pilot to put their shoulder harness on[10].
Up until now, everything was normal. Before leaving, the Captain simply said:
"Won't be long."
As security measures require, he closed the door carefully behind him. The Cabin Senior was already waiting for him in the galley.

In fact, she had already started working in front of door L1[11]. The pilot did not go far as the toilet was right next to the cockpit. Unfortunately, the "Occupied" sign was visible on the lock. He turned to the Flight Attendant for confirmation:

---

[9] Ever since the 9-11 terror attacks, the only procedure adopted by almost all airlines unanimously concerned cockpit security. If one of the pilots leaves the cockpit, a hostess or a steward is required to be near the door to keep an eye on access.

[10] When the aircraft is flying above 40,000 feet (Flight level 400) some airlines require the pilot remaining alone in the cockpit to put their oxygen mask on as sudden depressurisation and lack of oxygen can rapidly lead to loss of consciousness.

[11] The first door on the left of the cabin.

"Occupied?[12]"

"Yes, tough luck! A passenger's just gone in."

The Captain decided not to wait in front of the door.

"I'll come back later", he explained.

Up until now, all this was quite commonplace but everything was about to suddenly change. Just as the Captain was going to punch in his code number so he could return to the cockpit, he suddenly felt as though he was falling down a well: the floor gave way under his feet. Cries of panic from the passengers echoed around the cabin.

The Boeing had started to go into a dive.

A few seconds earlier in the cockpit, the First Officer had made a huge gaffe. Seeking a comfortable position to fill in his documents while being able to watch over the controls, he decided to pull his seat forward. As car drivers we are used to slipping our hands under the seat and pulling on the lever to change position in relation to the steering wheel. This is a simple operation but here the First Officer proved to be extremely clumsy. As he slid his seat forwards, he let it go too far on the runners and found himself shoved right up against the control column. His reaction was to push back on it vigorously. The result was immediate. The aircraft set off into a pronounced dive. The shock was so brutal that the Autopilot cut off the "altitude hold" mode immediately (the system is in fact designed not to resist if the pilot really insists on taking over the controls).

At first, the pressure exerted by First Officer was 20 pounds[13].

At **21:53:22** an alarm sounded in the cockpit as the Autopilot was no longer able to hold the aircraft's altitude. Unfortunately this two-tone alarm had the effect of an electric shock on the unlucky First Officer. The young man panicked and tried by all means available to push his seat back. He leaned forward but could not find the lever to ease himself backwards. His movements became increasingly chaotic and the only way he found to seek release was by pushing against anything within reach. And what was easiest to reach was precisely the most sensitive element - *the control column.*

---

[12] These exchanges outside the cockpit were obviously not recorded by the black box but reported to the investigators by those concerned afterwards.

[13] The Boeing controls are fitted with sensors that detect the force applied to the controls by each pilot.

At **21:53:35**, a pressure of 50 lb was applied to the controls. The result was immediate: the dive increased. Worse still, the more the aircraft dived, the more the First Officer lost his balance and the harder he leaned down against the instrument panel, trying his utmost to hold onto that *"something"* that was in front of him, pushing down with ever greater force on the column. This vicious circle brought the pitch-down attitude to -22°. By way of a comparison, during a normal landing, the angle of descent to the runway is just 3 degrees[14]. In these conditions, the airspeed rose dramatically with the Mach Number reaching 0.82[15.] The "overspeed" alarm went off immediately.

A second later, the First Officer again pushed even harder on the column and the aircraft started to go over into negative Gs. This meant that the passengers were in a situation of weightlessness. In the cabin, anything that was not fastened down flew into the air, including mugs, the greasy meal cartons, magazines and clothing. Everything started floating slowly up to the ceiling.
Then suddenly the dive decreased by a couple of degrees. The situation seemed to be recovering.
Everything floating around slowly fell back down onto the passengers. For five short seconds the First Officer had managed to bring the column backwards a little. The black box recorded that the attitude went back up to -20 degrees... But this did not last. Another loss of balance, more confusion, and the young man was once again jammed between his seat and the column... The weight of his body was pushing forwards and the deadly plunge started all over again...
In the cabin, the passengers were howling louder and louder with fear.
But worse was to come. In his panic, the First Officer then pushed down to the left and set the aircraft off into a turn. The Boeing was not just diving but also banking. This was the beginning of a manoeuvre that specialists call a "spiral dive", something that always leads to tragedy when a beginner is at the controls.

The whole scene would make for a good comedy film gag, with the clumsy pilot desperately waving his arms about between his seat and the instrument panel. However, this was for real. Lives were at stake with the aircraft's altimeter reading dropping at full speed as it hurtled down to the ocean surface.

---

[14] This is in fact an approach trajectory and not an attitude, but the comparison is still applicable.
[15] 82% of the speed of sound.

Cockpit door seen from the outside (note the keypad on the right).

On the other side of the door, the Captain had naturally understood the dramatic turn of events. But he was still off balance. His feet were hovering over the cabin floor and the only thing he could do was hang onto the "L1" Jump Seat harness. It was then that he saw that the Flight Attendant could help as she was just next to the keypad.

"Open the door, quick!" he yelled.
At first, the attendant was unable to respond as she had difficulty in standing up. The Captain insisted:
"Tell him to open the door, quick... right away!"
Before continuing with this account, some details about cockpits and their security systems are needed. Ever since 9/11, cockpit doors have been armoured and there is no way trying to break the door down with your shoulder is going to work as it did in the past. The cockpit door is now opened using a keypad similar to the ones found on any building entrance. The Flight Attendant therefore had three ways of getting into the cockpit:

- She could use the "Cockpit Entry Call". This is a simple code, consisting of a single figure, after which you press the "Enter" key. But this code does not open the door. That would be too simple... It triggers off a chime inside the cockpit. On more recent aircraft, a camera films the person in front of the door and their picture appears on a screen located to the right of the Captain. He can then press a switch to unlock the door. For safety's sake, most aircraft are now also equipped with a peephole.
- She could also use the interphone to call the flight deck and ask for the door to be opened.
- And then, there is the last solution. In an emergency, she can use the "Emergency Access Code"[16] enabling you to open the door from the outside. This special code is generally known to only three people aboard the aircraft: the Captain, the First Officer and the Cabin Senior. Even the other Flight Attendants do not know it. For obvious security reasons, the code is changed frequently.

---

[16] The Emergency Access Code is set by the airline, which generally uses the same code for each type of aircraft. Unlike the Cockpit Entry Code, it has a long series of figures (no letters). Not all crew know it.

The door seen from the inside of the cockpit.
On the lower part of the door is the "Kick Panel", an emergency exit that can be sprung with a kick once you have removed the two safety pins that can be seen on either side.

The Cabin Senior obeyed the Captain's instructions. She punched in the code, "1 + enter" to ask the First Officer to open the door by pressing the button.

But there was no response.

Panicking, she repeated the operation a number of times but to no avail. Seizing the telephone receiver, she called the cockpit. But the First Officer still failed to react.

Meanwhile the aircraft continued to dive.

At that moment the Captain managed to reach the keypad. He had to hurry as things were now getting dramatically out of control.

There was an incredible din in the cockpit. First of all, there was the whooshing noise of the airflow, getting louder as the speed increased. Then, there were the door chimes ringing out repeatedly caused by the Flight Attendant calling for the door to be opened plus a second chime when she tried to reach the First Officer on the interphone. But more than all that there were all the aircraft alarms going off on all sides - the overspeed horns, the autopilot warning of the rapid decrease in altitude, the MMO alarm and so on. All this created a dramatic acoustic environment that threw the First Officer into an even greater panic. Entangled in the controls, he was completely powerless.

His only reaction was to cry out for help.

"I can't manage!"

"Come and help me!"

"I can't!"

However, the door was still shut and as the First Officer made no attempt to open it, nobody could help him. He was unable to open the door or answer the Flight Attendant's calls, let alone stabilise the aircraft. When listening to the black box later, some investigators likened the state of panic overcoming the young man to hysteria.

Finally the Captain managed to punch in the Emergency Access Code and the door opened.

He rushed in.

It took him only a fraction of a second to realise that things were even worse than he had imagined. The aircraft was now engaged in a -26° dive. The moving marker on the speed indicator was now in the red. The aircraft was banking 5 degrees to the left. The Mach overspeed clacker sounded with its ugly and pervasive tack-tack-tack-tack ratchet-sounding noise[17].

---

[17] The MMO overspeed clacker is an alarm intended to warn the crew that the aircraft is going beyond its operational Mach number. Its ratchet sound is deliberately unpleasant so as to convey the danger of the situation.

All this meant just one thing: in a few seconds they would all be dead. Even before stepping over to the central console, the Captain could not hold back from shouting angrily:

"What the bloody hell are you doing?"

The only answer from the First Officer was a sort of cry and then he reacted almost childishly:

"It's not me, it's that thing..."

"Are you completely barmy?"

"I..."

"Let go of everything..."

With one hand holding onto the ceiling, the Captain managed to get back into his seat. This was all the easier as his control column was pushed forward and his own seat was pushed right back. He did not have to reduce the throttle. The computer had detected the overspeed and the two autothrottle levers had reversed by themselves.

But otherwise the whole situation was catastrophic!

Obviously his first reaction was to try and pull the column backwards. But the controls resisted. They seemed as if embedded in concrete. In fact, the First Officer was still pushing down in the opposite direction. What ensued resembled a wrestling match, with one of them pulling while the other was pushing and gesticulating wildly as he pushed against the back of his seat.

Spurred on by the energy of despair, the Captain used all the strength he could muster and at **21:54:19** the black box sensors recorded that the left-hand joystick was being pulled back with a force of 125 pounds. But still nothing happened.

Beside himself with rage, the Captain screamed:

"Let me have it!"

In fact, all his efforts had so far been in vain since the First Officer was pushing on the column even more vigorously than he was. As incredible as it may seem, at this moment, the sensor for the right-hand position recorded a pressure of *more than 200 pounds!* The situation was one of total panic!

"Idiot, leave it to me!"

"I can't..."

"Leave it... Leave it."

But the First Officer remained completely panic-stricken. He was still trying to get out and in so doing he kept pushing the column forward. Despite all his efforts, the Captain only managed to reduce the nose-down pitch attitude by 3 degrees.

Meanwhile the Flight Attendant managed to get seated in the jump seat. She put her harness on over her shoulders and shouted instructions to the passengers sitting in the front rows:

"Fasten your seat belts... Fasten your seat belts".

Then in the following second, she twisted round with her left arm and knocked on the washroom door just behind her to tell the passenger who was still in there to come out. She screamed even louder:

"Come out at once and go and sit down!"

A few seconds later the passenger managed to open the door and emerged looking dreadfully pale.

Initially, he resolved to go back to his own seat to the rear of the cabin. However, his efforts were to no avail. He was knocked completely off-balance and had trouble walking along the floor that kept giving way under his feet. The stewardess ordered him to go no further and, without hesitating, she opened the jump seat next to her and got him to sit down beside her. This seat was normally reserved for the crew but these were exceptional circumstances. The man was on the brink of having an attack and dropped onto the seat. She put the harness on him, shouting: "Don't move. Everything's going to be okay." She later admitted she did not believe a word of what she was saying and was convinced they were all going to die.

At **21:54:07**, the parameters recorded by the FDR were as follows:

- The dive attitude was -23 degrees.

- The aircraft was plunging towards the ground at Mach 0.89, which was well over the MMO.

Then suddenly the Captain managed to get the better of the First Officer. The nose of the aircraft started to pick up gradually. During the manoeuvre the aircraft was naturally subjected to an abnormal load factor and the passengers had to put up with a force of 2.2 Gs. They were being crushed down into their seats. They felt their cheeks being deformed. Some managed to cry out but most of them had difficulty breathing[18].

When the aircraft finally levelled out, the altimeter showed 30,200 ft. It had lost 7,000 ft during the misadventure[19]. This meant a fall of more than 1¼ miles – something to impress even the most experienced passengers.

---

[18] A force of 2.2 g is not much for a fighter pilot but extremely tough for an untrained airline passenger.

[19] 2,100 metres exactly

As soon as the aircraft came out of the dive, the Flight Attendant turned round and grabbed the interphone. She wanted to call the flight deck to find out what was going on but nobody replied. She understood the Captain had his hands full and did not insist.

Time went by but the atmosphere remained fraught with anguish… The passengers were totally silent. Nobody asked any questions but it was obvious that they were all terrorised at the idea of the aircraft starting to dive again. A few feet away in the front row a man had adopted the brace position and remained perfectly motionless. He later explained that he was certain he was about to die.

Five minutes later, the Flight Attendant decided to call the cockpit again.

Still no answer.

She wanted to get up and go to the door but the "Fasten your seat belts" was still on, so she remained where she was, waiting for instructions.

The Captain was busy getting back in control of the aircraft and taking stock of the situation.

Once the Boeing stabilised, it adopted a climb attitude to regain its cruising altitude of 37,000 ft. While the aircraft was climbing, the Captain tried to assess the damage. Strangely enough, everything still seemed to be operational. Pressurisation was nominal and the engines were running normally. The First Officer next to him had finally managed to push his seat back but remained motionless. When the chimes sounded, he did not even touch the microphone. His superior called him all the names under the sun, clearly expressing doubts as to his professional competence.

"You're out of your bloody mind!"

The Captain remained unconvinced when, to justify himself, the First Officer claimed he was at a loss to understand what had happened.

They had to return to 37,000 ft again but the Captain also had to report in to control. The Mumbai controller had seen the altitude suddenly drop on his radar. How could the Captain explain the fact that the aircraft had plunged 7,000 ft and was no longer on course? How could he possibly say on the active frequency that his First Officer had got stuck in the controls while he himself had gone to the toilet? A lot of other traffic was listening in on the same frequency and some pilots would burst out with laughter if they heard the truth of the matter. Carefully choosing his words, he simply announced that they had encountered a technical problem but that everything was now under control.

Naturally this explanation failed to satisfy the authorities who wanted to know more, fearing an accident on landing. But the Captain remained discrete with an enigmatic: "All's well now."

At **22:01:10**, the aircraft levelled out at on its initial cruising level. The entire incident had lasted exactly 8 minutes. A few moments later, the Cabin Senior tried to determine whether there had been any damage. She called one of the hostesses at the rear over the interphone:

"Any problems your end?"

The other girl confirmed that there were no casualties. Another attempt to get in touch with the cockpit remained fruitless. The Cabin Senior got up from her jump seat and went around the cabin talking to the passengers one by one to reassure them. Despite not knowing what had really happened, she reacted with considerable professional aplomb and managed to improvise: "It was just a technical incident. Everything's all right now. The pilots have the situation under control."

But she also realised that they had all been incredibly lucky. At the precise moment the aircraft dived, everybody's belt was fastened and there was only material damage of no real importance. The passengers had been eating and a lot of the meal cartons had been scattered all over the place. There would be a big dry cleaning bill, especially as the plastic goblets of sugary soda had flown in all directions during the dive, showering all over those nearby. Fortunately for the airline, the Indian clientele was remarkably philosophical and there would be no complaints.

Five minutes later, the Cabin Senior at last managed to get in touch with the flight deck.

"Is everything alright, Captain?"

"Yes, we're safe and sound. Everything's okay. And what about you, how are things back there in the cabin?

"We were lucky, they were all seated. There aren't any casualties. Er... you ought to say a few words to the passengers just to reassure them."

The Captain agreed.

"Okay, will do. Just let me finish what I'm doing and I'll speak to them in a moment."

At **22:04**, the Captain spoke over the Public Address system. His message was as follows:

"Ladies and gentlemen, this is your Captain speaking... We've just gone through a very large air pocket; this explains the very sharp loss of altitude which you felt... Er... But... Everything's alright now. Things are in order again and we shall be landing at Puna normally. Our landing is scheduled for, in... Er... about an hour."

There was a moment of silence before he added in rather an embarrassed tone of voice:

"I hope that despite this incident, er... which was quite beyond our control, you are satisfied with your flight aboard Air India Express."

After this announcement the passengers started to relax. A lot of them made attempts to clean their clothes. The hostesses quickly busied themselves with tidying up the mess and setting things right. There were bottles, plastic bags and cartons everywhere. To the rear of the cabin a trolley had been knocked over.

A quarter of an hour later, the Cabin Senior called the flight deck again.

"Can we resume serving, chief?"

"Yes, work normally. There's no further danger."

They commenced descent on time and even landed at Puna a few minutes early. The passengers disembarked without any problems but the aircraft was not cleared to take off for the next flight on the airline's schedule but grounded due to the incident. The whole affair had stirred things up and the authorities and technical services wanted to scrutinise the airplane. A backup aircraft was scheduled to continue the rotation but with a different crew. The Captain and the First Officer were taken off the roster to await the result of the enquiry.

Luckily the 737-800 is a sturdy aircraft. After a three-day long inspection, it was allowed to fly again.

The Indian DGCA[20] investigators concluded their report by saying that the aircraft recovered just in time as it was only a matter of a few more seconds before the incident would have ended in a catastrophe. If the dive had not been brought back under control, the Boeing would have broken up in flight. In the lower layers of the atmosphere it is likely the tail would not have resisted the overspeed but have started vibrating and then broken off.

---

[20] Directorate General of Civil Aviation.

Despite the evidence from the black boxes and the Captain, the First Officer fiercely denied any responsibility for what had happened. He claimed that the Autopilot had suddenly got everything mixed up. The aircraft had gone into a dive by itself and he had been unable to recover. He claimed he had tried reducing speed by diminishing the thrust, but in reality this was due to the auto-throttle working normally.

With disconcerting insincerity, he also claimed that he had called the Captain using the hostess call button "4 or 5 times". However there was no trace of these calls on the CVR recordings. He also claimed that he had tried to get up from his seat to open the door. However, he was unable to explain why he failed to just press the button within easy reach of his left hand. The physical and psychological tests he was subjected to revealed nothing significant.

After such a blunder, you might expect that the airline would have taken sanctions against the First Officer. However, following a hearing before a disciplinary committee, the young pilot was just temporarily suspended before being required to follow a training course and an in-flight check to confirm his capacities. In airlines with a stricter approach to things his misconduct (with potentially fatal consequences) would have led to immediate dismissal. Air India Express would seem to be rather more lax in its approach (and as already stated, they were short of pilots). The young man also appears to have benefited from support in high places as the investigators proved to be astonishingly indulgent towards him. Although the First Officer explained that he had made a serious mistake and had panicked, also admitting in veiled terms that he had not told the whole truth, they stated in their report that he would not be held to account in their submission made to the Indian Civil Aviation Authority.

This incident had a seriously damaging effect on Air India Express's image, already tarnished by an accident that had occurred four days earlier. One of their Boeing 737s had left Dubai later to crash at Mangalore. This was the same type of aircraft with the same superb artwork, and the same incredible causes... except this time there were 158 victims (see next chapter).

SLEEP

Saturday 22 May 2010

The aircraft was a Boeing 737-800, exactly the same model as the one in the previous story and belonging to the same operator, Air India Express. Everything said previously about that airline still applies[1].

These events took place four days before the pilot of the Dubai-Puna flight got entangled in his aircraft's controls. The next story is just as incredible but, sadly, the result was tragic.

Photo of the Boeing 737-800 in this story, registered VT-AXV.

The aircraft was registered in India as VT-AXV and like VT-AXJ in the previous account, its tail bore a superb frieze. This one was even more stunning as there were two different motifs, one on either side of the tail. On the right was the Temple at Koranak dedicated to the Sun and on the left the Victoria Memorial. Like the previous Boeing, it attracted huge attention from tourists stunned by the outstanding quality of its decoration.

It was almost new, having seen only two years service at the time of the events.

That night, it was flying between Dubai and Mangalore over a distance of 1,562 miles. A relatively short flight then, taking just 3¼ hours.

---

[1] The airline operates 10 Boeing 737-800s and a 747-400 Jumbo Jet all decorated in the same manner.

The passengers here too were mostly male migrant workers returning once and for all to their home country. The in-flight service offered the same type of free meal served in disposable containers. All the passengers had taken full advantage of Air India Express's particularly aggressive commercial policy with these destinations whereby, to attract customers, it allows 30 kilos of luggage per person in the hold at no extra charge! This is absolutely unique for a low-cost airline. Even "legacy" operators keep this type of privilege for their first class passengers. Indeed, for most airlines, hold luggage weight is limited to 20 kilos, sometimes even less. Any excess baggage is subject to a stiff surcharge[2].

Even more surprisingly, Air India Express sets no weight limit for cabin luggage, so you often see passengers struggling to stuff their effects into the overhead lockers. The marketing executives' understanding of their Indian customers, who tend to travel with a lot of luggage, led them to disregard loading issues as an excellent way to gain a competitive edge over their rivals.

The problem with this new policy was that it raised safety concerns: Air India Express aircraft were always very heavily laden and this was an issue in the factors that led to the accident.

Besides the aircraft was extra heavy for two other reasons:

- It was almost full.

- The airline wanted to save money on fuel, so it asked the crew to fill up in the Emirates, where kerosene is cheaper than in India. The Boeing therefore had more than 20 tons of fuel in its tanks[3]. This was almost double what the trip needed. There was no problem taking off at Dubai since Runway "12 Left" is 13,124 feet long[4] but this fact also played its part in the way events turned out.

There were 160 passengers aboard together with 6 crew members[5]. At check-in, there were 169 passengers on the list, but 9 of them turned up very late at the desk. They were turned away and told that their tickets would not be refunded. Little did they realise how lucky they were as they complained vociferously about the airline's harsh policy.

---

[2] The average price is 10 Euros per kilo of excess baggage.

[3] 20.6 tons exactly.

[4] As is the case throughout the United Arab Emirates, Runway 12L/30R is much longer than what is generally found around the world, being 4,360 yards long by 70 yards wide. Average dimensions are 3,270 yards by 49 yards.

[5] Among the aircraft's passengers, 164 were Indian, one was from Bangladesh and the Captain was Serb.

THE CREW

The **Captain** was Zlatko Glusica, 56, a Serb[6] from Bela Crkva. He had logged 10,215 flying hours mainly with JAT Yugoslav Airlines, then with JAT Airways[7]. He had only been working for Air India Charters Limited since 2008. He was said to be an experienced professional but a man who enjoyed life to the full and was often ready to party. He lived in Frankfurt and went to India each time he set off on a rotation for the airline. On leave he would go back to his wife and three children. He had arrived from Germany as a simple passenger the previous day.

First Officer Habinder Singh Ahluwalia was a Sikh and his situation was somewhat indeterminate. Although he was qualified as a Captain, the airline considered him a bit too inexperienced to take on the full responsibilities of the job. So he flew as First Officer. As mentioned, Air India Express sought, for reasons of image, to give priority to Indian pilots. Some young pilots' training was therefore speeded up to prove to its customers that it employed Indian pilots. But in practice it tended to entrust its aircraft to foreign, more experienced aviators.

Habinder Singh Ahluwalia respected Sikh religious traditions and wore a turban over his uncut hair and, just like Sikh bus drivers, he retained the headgear even when he was at the controls of an aircraft[8].

Ahluwalia was 40 and had logged some 3,619 flying hours. This was not much for a Captain but his professional record was excellent. Indeed, he had obtained the best results of his intake during recruitment tests. Moreover, and this was very rare, ever since the beginning of his career as trainee pilot, he had done nearly all his flying hours on Boeing 737-800s[9].

The young Ahluwalia had always been keen to be a pilot. This was his childhood dream and, as he himself had put it, that dream had "almost" been fulfilled. The main obstacle to his happiness came from his family who urged him to quit this job which they considered to be "very dangerous". His mother wanted him to take over the family business making exhaust pipes for Mahindra Cars.

---

[6] He had also taken out British citizenship.

[7] The airline changed its name in 1992 after the break-up of Yugoslavia.

[8] Wearing the turban (or pagri) is compulsory for Amritdhari (initiated) Sikhs. Forbidding them to do so is recognised in many countries as a form of religious persecution.

[9] The First Officer logged 3,319 hours on Boeing out of a total of 3,619 hours.

"*It's more profitable and less dangerous!*" his brother kept telling him, himself petrified at the idea of flying anywhere by aircraft. To bring him around, his mother encouraged him to get married and start a family. As was the custom, she had already found him a fiancée and wanted him to set a date for the wedding. But Ahluwalia was not at all ready to get married. He was a confirmed bachelor; he had just bought a flat and he had no intention of giving way to family pressure. He liked his job too much and he was good at it, too. Even though he had the reputation with his colleagues of not being easy to deal with, everybody recognised that he was meticulous and that he was a stickler for procedure. He was reported to have said to those around him that he "couldn't stand people who did things any old how in the cockpit".

This attitude perhaps explains how Ahluwalia came to be at the origin of an unprecedented conflict within the airline. A few weeks earlier, he had made an official complaint about a Captain who, according to him, had bungled his work. This man too was a Serb. The issue caused a certain amount of ill-feeling among the flight crews. An inquiry had been launched but the findings had not yet been made public and so no measures had yet been taken against the Captain concerned. However, it is clear that relations between those two men must have become particularly sour. Those responsible for drawing up the schedules decided as a precaution never to put them together in the same cockpit again.

There is nothing anecdotal in these background details. They all played a part, even indirectly, in how relations between the First Officer and his new Captain on the flight we are discussing here evolved, with tragic consequences.

The cabin crew that night included four attendants: two stewards and two stewardesses.
   - Mohamed Ali: Cabin Senior.
   - Yugantar Rana: Steward.
   - Sujata Siddarth Survase: Stewardess
   - Tejal Anil Kamulkar: Stewardess.

THE DESTINATION AIRPORT

Bajpe-Mangalore is ranked as one of the most difficult airports in India, being recognised by the Indian DGAC as one of India's seven "critical airfields". Strangely enough, new pilots do not immediately realise that the spot is dangerous. It is situated on the edge of the Indian Ocean and at first sight the approach is easy. In reality, there are a large number of parameters that make the landing complicated for airliners.

- Firstly, the runway is short, being just 2,217 yards long. This is not particularly dramatic, this distance being obviously long enough for a Boeing 737-800 to land and take off. However, the aircraft must not be too heavy, especially if the outside temperature is high[10].

- The approach path for Runway 24 is surrounded by rather high hills. The presence of this relief to the north-east prevents the pilot from stabilising a long way off for the final approach. The approach has to be carried out in the form of a DME arc (see the pullout below). This arc must be followed at a constant distance from the marker. Without being insurmountable, this procedure is somewhat trickier than the conventional flight path. Although the Boeing 737-800 is fitted with sophisticated navigation systems, the pilot has to concentrate more than if he were making a standard approach.

- More dangerously, the airport is situated on a sort of plateau. Towards the south-west, the end of Runway 24 gives way to a sharp slope and a drop of some 200 feet. On the other side, at the end of runway 06, there is a 250-foot drop. In aeronautical jargon, the runway is called a "table-top"[11]. Going off the edge of the concrete strip can only lead to disaster.

- Even more worrying, for aircraft heading south-west, Runway 24 is on a slight downward slope, meaning that braking has less effect.

- And to crown it all, the colour of the runways at Mangalore is very washed-out. The tarmac is almost blanched and the central markings are hard to make out while the figures indicating the magnetic direction of the runway simply do not exist.

For all these reasons the DGCA, the Indian civil aviation authority and most airlines disallow First Officers from taking the controls

---

[10]Air temperature is one of the parameters that influence take off and landings distances. The hotter it is, the longer those distances.

[11]There are two other "table top" airports in India - Kozhikode and Lengpui.

during landing and take-off at Mangalore. Only Captains can fly the aircraft.

All these difficulties failed to discourage the airport authorities from building a new terminal there. This was a year before the events recounted here took place. These ultra-modern buildings unfortunately have no positive influence on runway conditions and airlines are still reluctant to fly to Mangalore. At the time of writing, only four still operate there.

Flight IX 812 left Terminal 2 at 01.05 hours[12]. The night was pitch black. Take-off was at 01.35 hours. The aircraft was cleared to climb directly to Level 370 with a heading of 150. First it flew over the Sultanate of Oman as far as Muscat before setting out over the Arabian Sea before the long haul over the Indian Ocean to its destination.

In the cockpit, the Serb Captain and the Indian First Officer hardly spoke to each other. Barely acquainted, the two men belonged to two quite different worlds. How could the Serb possibly understand that Alhuwalia had to marry a woman his mother had chosen for him? As for Ahluwalia, what could he know about this former Yugoslav communist who now lived in a capitalist country and worked in India? Besides, neither of them was speaking in his native language. When they did speak to each other, it was in English and the exchanges were limited to technicalities as they went through a checklist. Even from a professional point of view, they had nothing to say to each other. Here again, job-wise, they were worlds apart. The Serb was aware the airline held no future for him as they had let it be known they wanted to replace him shortly. Things were quite different for the Sikh. He knew he would be staying with Air India Express[13]. Even better, if all went well for him, he would soon be leaving the low-cost subsidiary to join the parent airline, Air India. To work for the prestigious flag carrier was the dream of all Indian crews.

For the time being, unfortunately, he had to bide his time. For this flight as for all the others, he was only First Officer and had to obey his Captain. Technically the two men had almost nothing to say to each other on the particular challenges this flight represented. Both knew the route by heart. The Captain had already done it 19

---

[12] Dubai local time. As the Emirates are at UTC +4, take-off was at 21.25 hours GMT. To make the narrative easier to follow all times will be indicated in Dubai local time. The approach and landing will be shown in Mangalore local time.

[13] The First Officer was recruited on 27 April 2009.

times, while the First Officer had made the landing 66 times, even though he had never taken over the controls. He was therefore aware of all the difficulties it entailed.

The sense of routine was so pronounced that the Captain did not even bother to give his First Officer any instructions. As the climb started, he handed the aircraft over to him and took no further interest in the work. As a general rule, on a normal flight, the Captain and his First Officer share the tasks between them. One, as PF[14], takes the controls while the other, as Pilot Not Flying (PNF[15]), looks after radiocommunications. On each different flight, the Captain and the First Officer exchange functions so they can both maintain their level of proficiency. But that night the Captain decided he was going to take it easy. He handed over both functions (PF and PNF) to Ahluwalia. It was therefore the First Officer who spoke with control *and* who kept an eye on navigation and radiocommunications.

The 737-800 is one of Boeing's finest aircraft and this one was a recent NG (New Generation) model equipped with two autopilots that do just about everything. They manage engine power, maintain flight attitude and look after navigation right up to the final destination. They can even put the aircraft in the landing "stack" if the crew does not override them.

Radio exchanges that night were straightforward. Navigation was almost entirely over the Indian Ocean and the night-time traffic was light so although Ahluwalia had all the work to do, he was hardly under pressure.

At 02.05 hours in the morning the aircraft levelled out at 37,000 feet. Arrival at Mangalore was estimated at 06.25 hours[16]. The silence reigning in the cockpit was oppressive. Not the slightest exchange between the two men in the cockpit was recorded for more than an hour by the Cockpit Voice Recorder - just the rustle of files being opened and closed and the clicking of switches.

Then at around 3 o'clock, the Captain fell asleep... and the least that can be said is that his sleep didn't go unnoticed. Later when the NSTB investigators heard the recording[17], they stated that

---

[14] "Pilot Flying".

[15] "Pilot Not Flying".

[16] Mangalore local time (UTC +5½).

[17] The National Transportation Safety Board - the American enquiry organisation in charge of accident investigations.

"it was the first time that they'd ever heard a pilot snoring on the flight deck." This was nothing to do with the calm breathing of a peaceful sleeper but rather a series of loud snorting noises overwhelming the cockpit and lasting exactly one hour and 33 minutes.

Meanwhile, the First Officer managed the flight and made a good job of it while even taking care on two occasions to reply softly, when control asked for his position, so as not to disturb interrupt his Captain's dreams.

At 6 o'clock[18] in the morning the aircraft was 180 nautical miles from Mangalore with the Captain still in the arms of Morpheus. The landing was due in half an hour and the aircraft was still at its 37,000 feet cruising altitude. For the First Officer, it was now time to switch over to Mangalore approach frequency: 127.55 MHz. Here is the transcript of the conversation with the air controllers:

At **06:02:48 (First Officer):** *Mangalore control... Express India 812, good morning.*

The air controller's response was immediate. Mangalore is a small airport and there was no rush hour.

06:02:50 (Mangalore approach): *Express India 812, control, good morning. Go ahead.*

06:02:59 (First Officer): *Flight level 370, squawking 0544, and approaching IGAMA point... 812[19]*

06:03:02 (Mangalore approach): *Express India 812, Roger, report IGAMA.*

06:03:05 (First Officer): *Call you IGAMA, Express India 812.*

In the early hours of the morning the controller was probably tired too. In all events, he seemed to lack initiative. He only had two aircraft to supervise but nonetheless insisted that Flight 812 call him back when it passed over IGAMA, even though the First Officer had just told him they were almost over it. The fact that Mangalore approach radar had broken down a few days earlier might partially explain why the man seemed to be at a loss without it.

---

[18] Times are now expressed in Mangalore local time.
[19] Point IGAMA is 203 miles west of Mangalore, in the Indian Ocean.

Nothing happened for *12 seconds* before the First Officer called back.

06:03:17 (First Officer): *Mangalore, Express 812, position now over IGAMA point, Flight Level 370...*

06:03:20 (Mangalore approach): *Express India 812, control... er... Roger*

Four minutes went by before there was any further communication with the controller. Only the Captain's snoring left a trace on the flight recorder. No matter, the First Officer was working away as he wanted and was probably happy to be left alone to get on with things.

Now the aircraft was approaching its destination, he needed to obtain a weather report on the airfield. This was the end of May and weather conditions could prove awkward. Even though the monsoon was due to start in a month's time, it was already hot and there might be sudden rain.

06:07:02 (First Officer): *Mangalore control, Express 812, requesting latest Mangalore weather?*

06:07:06 (Mangalore approach): *Express India, Control... Here's Mangalore 0000 report: wind calm, visibility 6 kilometres... clouds few at 2,000 feet... temperature 27 degrees... dew point 26... and QNH 1006 hectopascals[20].*

It was dawn. As was often the case at this time of the year, the sun rose over a grey, hot and humid atmosphere and the temperature had already reached 27° C. Local forecasts had already predicted that a temperature of more than 38° C would be reached during the day. What was surprising however was that despite the high temperature, the dew point was 26. This meant that the weather was almost foggy[21].

---

[20] As is the rule in aeronautics, the controller uses GMT. The weather report which he gave was therefore the one that had just been published 7 minutes earlier.

[21] When the atmospheric temperature is the same as the dew point, tiny drops of water in suspension change into fog. In the present instance, with parameters 27/26, all that was needed was for the outside temperature to drop by one degree for visibility to be reduced radically.

06:07:18 (First Officer): *Understood, 1006 hectopascals and runway 24... and confirm we are identified on radar 812.*

06:07:22 (Mangalore approach): *Negative sir, radar not available.*

So now the First Officer was working alone in the cockpit, with the Captain snoring happily beside him and the aircraft about to land at one of the most difficult airports in India whose approach radar wasn't working. Given the circumstances, the crew should have held a briefing under the Captain's authority to make a number of major decisions. Obviously, no such thing took place. At first, the First Officer seemed happy to just acknowledge the information.

06:07:27 (First Officer): *Er... Roger... Express 812...*

Yet you could feel some hesitation. A no radar approach was not unfeasible. There are thousands of airports around the world not so equipped that receive aircraft every day. Except that, as already explained, Mangalore is not just any airport; the First Officer had to decide all by himself.
One long minute went by... his voice betrayed his unease as he ended up asking:

06:08:41 (First Officer): *Er... Mangalore Control... Express India 812... Er... what kind of approach can we expect for Runway 24 in Mangalore?*

This was no idle question. With no radar assistance, he had to choose the procedure that would best enable him to reach the final approach. It was something of a one-off since crews flying into Mangalore were usually guided by radar.
The answer was brief, laconic.

06:08:48 (Mangalore approach): *ILS - DME arc approach.*

06:08:50 (First Officer): *Roger, we're going to make an ILS DME Arc... Express 812... Er... We are ready for the descent.*

06:08:55 (Mangalore approach): *Standby... 812.*

The First Officer therefore maintained his level at 37,000 feet. Another silence in the cockpit punctuated only by the Captain snoring. A minute later, it was the controller's turn to ask a question. Its tenor showed that he too was not particularly alert that morning.

06:09:48 (Mangalore approach): *Express India 812, it's the control... Er... how far are you from IGAMA point? Express India 812...*

The First Officer was naturally surprised. He had flown over the IGAMA point just five minutes earlier. He had announced this clearly to the controller who had acknowledged the message.

06:09:55 (First Officer): *Express India 812, we've already checked IGAMA at 00:04.*

The controller reformulated his question so as not to appear too foolish.

06:10:04 (Mangalore control): *Er... Yes, well, so report distance flown from IGAMA?*

06:10:14 (First Officer): *Well... we're 48 nautical from inbound IGAMA[22].*

06:10:20 (Mangalore control): *Control Roger.*

A silence, then:

06:11:05 (Mangalore control): *Express India 812, call me for descent when you're on radial 287 and at 80 nautical miles from MML beacon[23].*

For some unknown reason, the controller was delaying the Boeing's descent. Was he being over-cautious to make sure it was kept away from other traffic? However, there were only two aircraft in his airspace and there was no reason to stress, even with a failed radar system. Moreover, the other flight was Air India Express

---

[22] 55 miles.

[23] MML Beacon: a VOR/DME beacon near Mangalore. In the original English text, the specialists noticed that the control made another mistake by asking for them to put off until 80 nautical miles, saying "from" instead of "until".

Flight 372 coming in from Bahrain and heading for Calicut[24] (after a stopover in Qatar). It had to descend too, but its flight path did not interfere with that of flight 812.

It remains unclear why the controller failed to let the Boeing descend. The situation was confused. In addition, the message was picked up by the wrong person as it was Flight 372's Captain who answered.

06:11:11 (Flight 372 Captain): *Understood Express India 372. We'll call you on radial 287 for the descent when we're 80 nautical miles from VOR MML.*

The controller suddenly realised he was no longer dealing with the right person and became irritable.

06:11:24 (Mangalore control): *Negative!!! Express India 812, from Mangalore Radar, call me when you're on radial 287 and 80 nautical miles from MML.*

06:11:25 (First Officer): *Roger… for your information, we're already on radial 287 and we'll call you at 80 nautical miles from MML for descent.*

06:11:39 (Mangalore control): *Affirm.*

As the Boeing was practically over the required position, it would have been normal for the controller to clear it to descend. However, he failed to respond. The outcome of this inexplicable delay turned out to be disastrous. Until now the First Officer had not made a single error. Although he was working alone, he had handled radiocommunication just fine and the aircraft was right on course. Ahluwalia was perfectly qualified to perform all the necessary tasks. All he needed was to be able to start his descent so he would not be too high when arriving at Mangalore.

Another five minutes went by; the Boeing maintained 37,000 feet. The greyish mass of the Indian Ocean slipped by rapidly under the wings.

06:16:54 (First Officer): *Mangalore control, Express India 812, we're 80 nautical miles on radial 287 from MML.*

---

[24] Calicut is 112 miles away on the coast south of Mangalore.

The First Officer was obviously hinting that he wanted to descend. But once again there was no reply. The controller was talking to the aircraft on approach to Calicut and it seemed to take quite a while before he showed any interest in Flight 812 again.

06:17:15 (Mangalore control): *Break, break[25] Express 812 from control?*

06:17:16 (First Officer): *812, we're now at 77 nautical miles DME inbound, sir...[26] Request start descent.*

06:17:20 (Mangalore control): *812, from control, maintain radial 287 from MML. Descend to 7,000 feet and report leaving Fight Level 370.*

06:17:34 (First Officer): *Roger, descending 7,000 feet; we're leaving Level 370 just now... Express India 812.*

At last! In the same instant, the First Officer put out his hand towards the MCP under the instrument panel dash[27]. He scrolled for the function "Altitude" and replaced the figure 370 by 70. On the central console, the two auto-throttles moved slowly backwards and the Boeing's attitude decreased.
The figures started slipping by on the altimeter...
The descent had started.
On the Cockpit Voice Recorder, you could still hear the Captain snoring but with less regularity. Sometimes the breathing slowed down before becoming almost inaudible and then starting off again, as if the man had breathing problems. Some experts thought this was evidence of someone who was overweight. Others thought his nasal mucous membrane was swollen, perhaps signalling the beginning of a cold. One thing was certain: anyone snoring like that was not exactly stressed by his job.

The controller called three minutes later:

---

[25] Term used in aeronautical phraseology to signify a sudden change in interlocutor. The controller was speaking with Flight 372 and he cut his message with the word "break" to address Flight 812.
[26] 88 miles.
[27] The Mode Control Panel allows the most important functions on the Autopilot, such as speed, altitude, heading, vertical speed, vertical navigation, lateral navigation, etc. to be controlled automatically.

06:20:44 (Mangalore control): *Express India from control... report level?*

Notice how the controller forgot to state which aircraft he was addressing. He still had two Express India flights in his zone but failed to give the flight number. No matter, Ahluwalia was on the ball. He took it he was the one being spoken to:

06:20:48 (First Officer): *We are descending out level 295[28].*

You may be wondering why the First Officer did not rouse the Captain. The simple fact is that he did not need him. He was getting along fine by himself and was putting off the moment when he would have to hand over the controls. Naturally, he would have to relinquish in the end since the regulations forbade him from landing the aircraft. But there was no hurry for the moment! One can feel in Ahluwalia's attitude evidence of a certain level of frustration.

06:20:53 (Mangalore control): *Express India 812, Roger ... Call 50 nautical miles inbound MML[29].*

The Mangalore controller clearly seemed to be out of phase because the First Officer immediately retorted:

06:20:55 (First Officer): *For your information we're at 50 nautical miles inbound. Express India 812!*

06:20:58 (Mangalore control): *Roger.*

The Captain still slept as the Boeing got closer to the beacon, still flying too high.

06:24:20 (First Officer): *Mangalore... Express India 812, we are 25 nautical miles to MML[30].*

06:24:23 (Mangalore control): *Express India 812 from control... Continue descent to 2,900 feet. And contact the tower on 122.10.*

---

[28] 29,500 feet.
[29] 56¼ miles.
[30] 28¾ miles.

06:24:30 (First Officer): *Roger, sir... down to 2,900 feet and we contact the tower. Er... can we proceed directly to 338 radial DME?*

06:24:32 (Mangalore control): *Approved... Report your level now?*

06:24:36 (First Officer): *Out of level 184, sir[31].*

Once again, Ahluwalia was not to blame, but this time it was urgent! The aircraft was only 25 nautical miles from Mangalore but still at 18,400 feet!

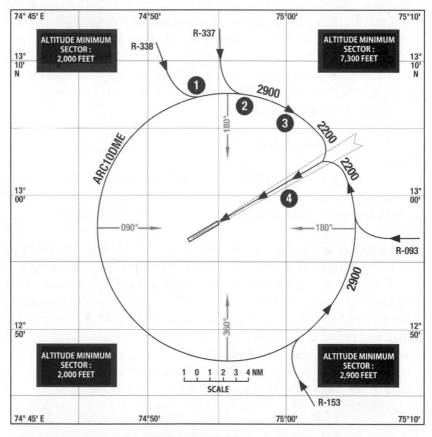

The Mangalore approach ILS 24 ARC DME as described on the sheet used by Air India Express. This type of approach was recommended for airports with awkward relief nearby. In the case of Mangalore, the aircraft has to describe the arc of a circle at 10 nautical miles (11¼ miles) from the airport before starting the final approach.

---

[31] 18,400 feet.

06:24:43 (Mangalore control): *OK... proceed to 338 radial. Call 12 nautical miles and contact the tower on 122.1.*

Radial 338 is clearly indicated on the approach pattern. The aircraft's flight path is easy to visualise. It was going to arrive from the north-west. When it was at 10 nautical miles, it would then make a turn to the left in order to describe the arc of a circle to bring it onto the final approach for Runway 24.

06:24:47 (First Officer): *122.10... Thank you... Express India 812.*

A sudden fit of coughing then echoed round the cockpit followed by a sonorous yawn and a groaning noise. The Captain was beginning to emerge... But the awakening was clearly rough for him. This was understandable in the circumstances as the man had been huddled up for one and a half hours now in a seat that was nowhere near as comfortable as his bed.
The first word he pronounced was an exclamation of surprise revealing his state of mind:
"*What?*"
That was all. The Serb had just awoken to the fact that he was not in his bedroom and that he would have to get down to work. Another yawn... but not a word was exchanged with the First Officer.

From now on, everything went very fast. At 343 mph the Boeing took just six short minutes to cover the last 31 miles to the airport. The Captain was awake but remained silent. Ahluwalia was doing all the work. Did the chief try to find out what the aircraft's position was? Was he watching the flight path seriously or was he struggling not to go back to sleep? We shall never know.
In fact, he barely heard his First Officer say:
"*The radar isn't working and I don't know what to do*".
A long silence then the Captain replied with a hoarse voice:
"*No problem!*"

But he still did not take over the controls. The First Officer's workload was now mounting up as he had to deal with a more complex flight path. Earlier, the aircraft had been on a level cruise but now the ground was getting closer and he had to follow the arc of a circle with great accuracy to reach the final approach. Although the autopilot was controlling the flight path, it would still have been better for both of them to be working together...

For some time now however, the aircraft's descent had been abnormal. It would go down at a normal rate before suddenly accelerating in a series of fits and starts. This jerky movement was due to the First Officer putting on the speed brakes several times to boost the rate of descent. However, he seemed hesitant, applying the speed brakes in short bursts - not in a sustained enough manner to bring the Boeing onto the correct vertical flight path.

Once again the CVR recorded a series of yawns. Still no words. The Captain was clearly having some difficulty waking up.

Dawn was rising and under the wings the view was gradually changing. Despite the altitude, a white line could be made out on the horizon. This was the crest of the waves stretching out of sight along the coastline. The greyish mass of the ocean was making way for the darker mass of land.

But the First Officer had no time to admire the view. On request from control, he switched frequency from 127.55 MHz to 122.10 MHz.

He contacted the control tower... And he was now starting to feel tired as, just before calling, he could not avoid giving off a long yawn.

06:24:51 (First Officer): *Mangalore Tower... Express India 812, good morning, sir.*

06:24:59 (Tower): *Express India 812, good morning... report established 10 nautical miles arc for Runway 24.*

06:25:00 (First Officer): *Roger, call you established 12 nautical miles arc runway 24.*

Was it due to early morning tiredness or overwork? The First Officer had just made a mistake. The controller picked up on it.

06:25:04 (Controller): *10 DME Arc!*

06:25:08 (First Officer): *Roger, 10 DME arc... Express 812.*

Two minutes later, the Boeing reached the arc (position 1 on the illustration). At that moment, it should have been at 2,900 feet[32]; instead it was still at more than 9,000 feet. As the approach sheet

---

[32] See illustration. This was the altitude above sea level. The height of this circuit in above the runway: 1,893 feet (575 m).

shows, he started his turn to the left to follow the arc of the circle which made him pass 11¼ miles to the north of the runway. Once he had stabilised on the turn (position 2 on the illustration), the First Officer was to call the tower.

When the altimeter indicated 8,500 feet, the Captain suddenly seemed to realise that the aircraft was much too high. He said hoarsely:
"Gear!"
Lowering the landing gear is an excellent way to slow an aircraft down and also increase the rate of descent. But this was still not enough and the First Officer continued to apply the speed brakes. However, the action remained intermittent as, inexplicably, he applied them in fits and starts.
For the time being the aircraft's altitude was not at all dangerous. If the crew were able to deal with the situation so that the aircraft was stabilised for the final approach, there would be no problem and the passengers would not notice anything untoward.

06:27:44 (First Officer): *Mangalore tower... Express India 812, we are established on 10 DME arc runway 24.*

06:27:52 (Tower): *Understood, Express India 812, report established on ILS.*

06:27:58 (First Officer): *Ok sir... Call you established on ILS... Express 812.*

Six minutes went by during which the Boeing described the arc marked 3 on the illustration. During this procedure, the aircraft ought to have been stabilised at 2,200 feet. It was actually still descending and never reached that altitude. Although Glusica was awake, Ahluwalia still did all the talking over the radio and he was the one flying the aircraft although he clearly understood that this state of affairs could not continue indefinitely. Airline regulations were strict: only the Captain was cleared to handle the controls for the landing at Mangalore.
Even so, the most basic rules safety would require both crew members to be operational during the approach phase. For the moment, this was far from being the case.
At about **06:30**, there were a few growling noises, then the CVR recorded the sound of sliding metal. The Captain was at last

readjusting his seat to take control of the aircraft. After a good hour and a half of sleep he should have been well refreshed!

At **06:32**, the Boeing started its last turn to the right so as to stabilise on the Runway 24 axis (position 4 on the illustration). The Autopilot was still flying the aircraft. A few seconds later, the localiser needle centred accurately on the FMS. The flight path would have been perfect if only the aircraft had not been so high.

The flaps were fully down, at 40 degrees and the speed brakes were applied. The three green lights were on, showing that the landing gear was down and locked. But all that was not enough to bring the aircraft onto a correct descent path. Unlike the previous series of Boeings[33], the Boeing 737-800 is extremely aerodynamic making it more difficult to slow down. Matters were not improving. The landing gear was down and the aircraft was vibrating gently but it was still not going down fast enough to reach the correct flight path. Another yawn in the cockpit...

The aircraft was now on the runway axis but it was more than 6,000 feet high. Perhaps the tension was mounting as the First Officer forgot to call the tower back as requested. So the controller called in.

06:34:15 (Tower): *Express India 812... Confirm, you are established on the ILS?*

06:34:17 (First Officer): *Er... Affirmative Express India 812...*

06:34:17 (Tower): *Wind calm, cleared to land Runway 24.*

06:34:22 (First Officer): *Clear to land, Express.*

You cannot help but note that the First Officer cheated a little here. The aircraft was not quite established on the ILS... Although it was indeed on the axis, it was far from being on the correct glide path.

The seconds went by and the Boeing was still high up on its approach. That would not have been a real problem if it had had a 12,000 foot long runway ahead of it, as can be found at some airports. But at Mangalore, the approach has to be made with the

---

[33] The previous 737 series (200, 300, 400, 500, 600 and 700) look like the 800 but from an aerodynamic point of view they are very different. The latest model is characterised by an exceptional lift to drag ratio, making for reduced fuel consumption.

greatest care. All you have to do is examine the lie of the land (see illustration) to see that the runway slopes away 500 yards after the threshold. If the aircraft failed to stabilise once and for all, the outcome would be tragic.

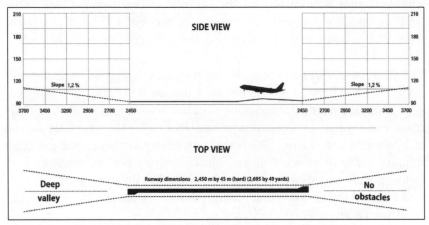

Longitudinal section of the Mangalore runway

The seconds ticked by and the Boeing was now 2½ miles from the runway. Thrust was reduced to the minimum but the aircraft was still at 2,500 feet, still much too high. The pullout shows that the ideal flight plan angle should be 3 degrees. Now, if the Captain wanted to reach the runway, he should have put the aircraft into twice that value at a 6-degree dive. The First Officer quite warned correctly:

"We're far too high!"

The Captain gave no answer but disconnected the Autopilot to take over. Once this was done, he pushed down further on the control column.

He wanted that runway and he was going to get it!

The First Officer disagreed. He was starting to have serious doubts and blurted out a second warning:

"The runway is straight ahead... er... below."

But the Captain persisted. Instead of calmly increasing power and doing a missed approach, he told himself he could make it and continued to push down. The aircraft dropped even more. But the laws of physics are incontrovertible and what it lost in height, it gained in speed.

The Boeing was accelerating!

06:35 (Captain): *Oh my God...[34]*

The investigators reckoned this exclamation was more an expression of astonishment than fear. It was probably at that precise moment that the Captain realised he was much too high to land. But instead of giving up, he made things worse. His reaction was particularly brutal, pushing pig-headedly even further down on the stick, going for the runway. Physicians who later studied this almost instinctive attitude concluded that ever since he had awoken Zlatko Glusica had not had enough time to adapt to the situation and that he was constantly out of sync.

Within two seconds the steady flight path changed into an impressive dive. The rate of descent reached 4,000 feet per minute. This was almost six times the normal approach rate. It was all the more insane in that, for some reason or other, he retracted the speed brakes while still pushing on the stick. Was this due to a mental glitch or an uncontrolled movement? Whatever the reason, under the circumstances, the speed just increased even further.
This time, the First Officer understood that this was really not going to work out. Quite logically he suggested:

06:35 (First Officer): *Go around Captain?*

This suggestion was expressed as a polite question. After all, there was still no immediate danger. It was nothing to be proud about, but all pilots have at one time or another missed an approach. Nothing serious. All you have to do is press the TOGA[35] button and the engines set off again at maximum power. The pitch attitude would return to positive and the aircraft would be off again all by itself.
As an answer, the Captain grunted incomprehensibly:

06:35 (Captain): *Bad loc... localiser... the glide.*

This made no sense! Glusica actually seemed to be confusing the approach axis with the glide approach... Was he really fully awake? The First Officer was obviously starting to get worried. Seeing his boss continuing to push on the stick, he reacted again.

---

[34] For some unexplained reason, the inquiry did not officially publish the exact timings of the CVR. The author has therefore left the time but without the seconds.
[35] *Take Off and Go Around*: pulling up and increasing thrust. Simply pressing this button gets the aircraft back climbing with maximum thrust from the two engines.

06:35 (First Officer): *Go around? We're not stabilised! Go around?*

Alhuwalia was perfectly correct... Since the aircraft was not stabilised for the final approach, they had to go around. The problem was that he himself did nothing to take over the controls. In this case, it would not have been insubordination. Airline rules gave him the right to do so. The texts say that *if the First Officer asks twice* for a go around and the Captain does not react, *he is authorised to do so himself.* In fact in the present case, not only did Ahluwalia have the right, but it had now become an acute safety matter. Unfortunately, he failed to act. Maybe he was scared of again coming into conflict with his Serbian Captain. Or perhaps he still thought his boss was going to manage. We shall never know... He stayed put.

In the cockpit, the EGPWS was going crazy:

EGPWS[36] **synthetic voice**: *Sink rate... Sink rate... Whoop whoop... Pull up... Whoop whoop pull up...*

The sink rate was so pronounced that the computer system considered that the aircraft was about to crash.
The EGPWS warning persisted.

EGPWS synthetic voice: *Sink rate... Sink rate... Whoop whoop Pull up... Whoop whoop pull up...*

For a few moments, the Captain told himself he was going to make it. With this dive, he had succeeded in losing enough altitude. He was going to get to that runway! The problem was that the aircraft had now stored up too much energy and this had been converted into speed. Despite the speed brakes, the landing gear and the flaps, the aircraft was hurtling along like a missile.
The figures spoke for themselves:
The Boeing crossed the runway threshold at 160 knots and a height of 200 feet[37]. Under normal circumstances this should have been 144 knots and 50 feet.
Too high and too fast!
This was all compounded by the fact that the aircraft was extremely heavy. There was still more than 8 tons of fuel in the tanks. And

---

[36] Enhanced Ground Proximity Warning System.
[37] 187 mph and 196 feet high when it should be 166 mph and 50 feet high.

then there was the luggage in the cargo compartment and every passenger's hand baggage making for another three tons.

EGPWS synthetic voice: *Sink rate... Sink rate... Whoop whoop Pull up... Whoop whoop pull up...*

As the aircraft plummeted, the Captain abruptly pulled on the stick to inflect the trajectory. But the aircraft refused to land. Due to its high speed, there was still too much lift. The aircraft continued flying along at low altitude. Then Glusica decided to force matters...

With a brutal forward movement of the stick, he forced the aircraft to make contact with the runway. This was no "kiss" but a brutal three-point landing after the aircraft had already covered 1,498 yards flying along over the runway.

Panic broke out in the cabin among the passengers as the touchdown was followed by a loud explosion. The impact had been so violent that one of the left landing gear tyres had burst, although this did not prevent the Boeing from bouncing upwards a hundred feet or so...

The First Officer intervened again immediately, no longer making a mild suggestion but shouting out:

06:34:38 (First Officer): *Go around, Captain! Go around Captain!*

Ahluwalia's voice betrayed his fear. Indeed, he was so frightened that he instinctively pressed the microphone transmit/receive button and his shouts echoed immediately inside the control tower. But the Captain had absolutely no intention of following his First Officer's advice but pushed down again on the stick to bring the aircraft back onto the runway.

The Boeing hit the ground for the second time and here there was no bounce effect. The airplane had already swallowed up 1,728 yards of the runway and there were only 948 left. This was all the shorter to slow down as the runway was on a slight downward slope.

During the next six seconds, Zlatko Glusica remained totally passive. He was hesitating: brake or increase the thrust and take off again? This hesitation was endless... 6 seconds during which the aircraft was going along at more than 125 mph. An eternity!

Finally Glusica decided to brake. He activated the thrust reversers and applied pressure to the brakes. The problem was that his action lacked conviction. The auto-brake selector was only on position 2 meaning that his braking was only average for a landing under such circumstances. The Boeing slowed down but not enough.

Investigators later went through a braking simulation at Boeing and made a surprising discovery. If the Captain had applied maximum emergency pressure to the brakes on touchdown, the aircraft would have stopped 100 yards short of the end of the runway. The situation was therefore extremely serious but not yet catastrophic.

Unfortunately, through the windshield, the end of the runway was quickly looming up. Glusica was still not braking energetically enough. When he finally understood he had made the wrong decision, he did exactly what he should not have done: *he changed his mind!*

Hesitantly, he ordered:

06:34:44 (Captain): *Go around!*

As he spoke these words, he pushed the throttle levers forward. This was a terrible mistake for at that very moment all the data showed it was too late to take off again:

- There were only 350 yards of runway left.
- The Captain had forgotten that the aircraft manufacturer did not authorise the pilot to pull up once thrust reverse was being used. The engine needed time for the clamshell doors to move back into place and for engine thrust to be effective.
- The outside temperature was high.
- The aircraft was heavy.
- And as if all that wasn't enough... it had a burst tyre.

However, unexpectedly, the thrust reversers quickly moved back into place and the Boeing started to speed up. Unfortunately it had no chance of being able to take off over such a short distance.

In the tower, the controller had still not realised what was happening. He had seen the Boeing touch down and thought it was going to come to a stop normally. He even started giving instructions to guide it to the air terminal.

06:35:04 (Tower): *Express India 812, backtrack runway 24 and vacate via taxiway Delta.*

There was no answer from the crew. Both engines were at full throttle but it was too late... The irony of the situation was that a few seconds earlier the Boeing was going too fast to land, now it was too slow to take off.

The end of the runway approached.

Once again the controller heard someone screaming over the radio. It was the First Officer shouting a sort of last cry for help.

06:35:21 (First Officer): *Control!!!*

There was nothing the controller could do for him. The Boeing reached the end of the runway at just 87 mph, much too slow for take-off, but it was still accelerating. It ploughed through a sand bunker and its right wing hit the localiser aerial. Another left landing gear tire burst. Then it went right through the airport perimeter fencing. Just behind that, there was the steep slope that dropped over 200 feet or so.

The aircraft plunged at full speed into thick forest and disappeared from the controller's sight.

06:39:29 (Tower): *Express India 812, from control... Express India 812... Mangalore tower.*

06:39:39 (Tower): *Express India 812... Mangalore tower...*

There was no answer.

Final time sequence during the accident

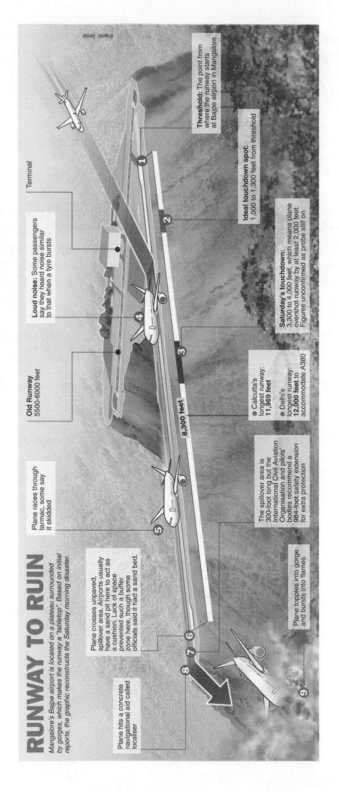

The scene inside the aircraft was apocalyptic. The seats seemed to slip away from under the passengers. The fuselage suffered a series of massive impacts with branches hitting the metal and scratching the windows with loud screeching sounds. Then, the cracking sounds got louder and louder and the airframe started to deform. The floor was torn apart... the passengers were screaming. In the front some of the seats were torn off their supports. Meanwhile, an awful burning smell invaded the cabin.

Suddenly flames burst out on the wings.

Joel de Souza was a 24 year-old Portuguese native of Mangalore. He was sitting in seat 23A. A few seconds later, he saw a clear liquid spurting up from the floor. At first, he thought the aircraft had fallen into a river but the liquid burst into flames under his feet. His trouser legs started to burn. The fire spread at top speed all around him. The carcass of the Boeing was still bumping down the slope and many of passengers were unfastening their seat belts to flee from the flames that were rapidly chasing up along the aisle. At that moment the young man thought he was going to die.

Then suddenly a miracle took place.

A huge crack opened out in the fuselage and a tear appeared in the partition right next to him. Within a second, it got bigger. De Souza leapt at the opportunity, letting himself drop down into the opening. At that moment, the wreck was still sliding down the slope at a speed the investigators estimated at 31 mph. The wings cut through the forest like a giant scythe.

The man fell onto a huge pile of branches, then slid down the slope... In his fall, he fractured his leg and a couple of vertebrae but felt no pain at the time. He managed to get up and fled into the undergrowth. It was then that he realised his shoes and trousers were on fire.

He was not alone in escaping from that hell. Six other passengers managed to throw themselves out through the rip in the fuselage. The last miraculous escapee only just got out of the aircraft before a gigantic fireball hurtled skywards... 8 tons of fuel had just caught fire. The blast of the explosion was so intense that the survivors were hurtled into the undergrowth.

The last survivors were not as lucky as de Souza. Some like KP Manikutty, Krishna or Stalin Mayakutti had their faces burnt. In these exceptional circumstances, there were eight survivors in all. Seven of them were seriously injured. Only one was practically unharmed.

The other occupants of the aircraft, including Captain Zlatko Glusica and First Officer Ahluwalia were all burnt alive, making a total of 158 victims.

The whole of India went through a trauma following the Air India Express Flight 812. The general public was all the more incensed in so far as people considered that if the First Officer had been cleared to fly the aircraft he might have saved it. The media treated him posthumously as a national hero.

As far as the Captain was concerned, the investigators later explained that his incredibly passive attitude was caused by his being in the wake-up phase. Only 9 minutes elapsed between the moment he opened his eyes and the moment he got back to work. It was too brief... The specialists talked of "inertial sleep and a perturbed circadian rhythm", a traumatism destabilising the internal clock of the brain in the hypothalamus. His judgment was completely distorted. Zlatko Glusica had simply not realised that his approach was much too high. Then, he also failed to grasp that the aircraft had not stabilised. Worse still, he convinced himself that he had to land the aircraft when all the parameters indicated that he had absolutely no chance of doing so successfully.

The peculiar geography of this "table-top" airport was obviously also put forward as being one of the causes of the drama. The radar breakdown was also mentioned, as were the controller's failings in guiding the aircraft in. But in reality, all these elements were only co-factors. The Mangalore crash was above all the result of a terrible human error. The person really responsible for the accident was the Captain, with his negligence.

This story cannot be wound up without discussing its surrealistic aftermath, one that must certainly remain unique in the annals of air crashes.

As is often the case after accidents, the airline tried to dissuade the survivors from suing it. Air India Express management found a novel means of doing so. In exchange for a written agreement never to take them to court, they offered them a job within the airline itself. In a country where holding down a stable job is considered to be an inestimable privilege, some of them accepted immediately...

STRESS and OVERSIGHT

Wednesday 20 August 2008
Madrid

It was 13.10 at Madrid-Barajas Airport. A Spanair DC-9-82 was waiting at gate T21[1]. The aircraft had just flown in from Barcelona that morning and was now getting ready to leave again for Las Palmas in the Canary Islands. The 166 passengers on board were mainly tourists seeking holiday sunshine, most of them Spaniards though many other nationalities were represented[2]

The DC-9-82 involved in this story (registration EC-HFP). The high-lift devices mentioned later can be seen clearly: the flaps deflected at 40 degrees on the trailing edges of the wings and the slats that increase the curve on the leading edges.

---

[1] The plane was a DC-9-82 whose technical designation was subsequently changed to "MD 82"

[2] Apart from 131 Spaniards there were twelve other nationalities (German, Brazilian, French, Mauritanian, Turkish, Bulgarian, Gambian, Italian, Chilean, Finnish and Swedish). A woman mentioned later even had dual Spanish and British nationality.

The aircraft bore the airline's new white and blue colours with the inscription "Star Alliance" written lengthwise on the fuselage. As is often the case, it also sported its own name discreetly under the cockpit window: "*Sunbreeze*". Most of Spanair's aircraft have this type of name involving the Sun: *Sunspot, Sunrise, Sunset, Sundowner*, etc.

The "Sunbreeze" in this story was registered as EC-HCP.

The **Captain** was Antonio Garcia Luna, 39, and the holder of an Airline Transport Pilot's Licence. He logged 8,746 flying hours of which three-quarters were on DC-9s. He had the reputation of being a serious man. Married and the father of two little girls, he lived in an attractive house on the coast in Majorca. A month earlier, he had been mentioned in a glowing newspaper report since he had had the honour of flying the Castellion football team out on a memorable trip.

Before being recruited by Spanair, Antonio Garcia Luna had flown in the Spanish Air Force at the controls of a small "Aviocar 200" on which he had carried out maritime reconnaissance and air/sea rescue missions. He was highly rated and was not known to have any problems.

He was the one who was going to pilot this DC-9 as PF for this flight.

The **First Officer** was Javier Francisco Mulet. He had initially flown for *Iberworld,* a charter operator, for a number of months before being recruited as First Officer with Spanair. He had only chalked up 1,000 flying hours and did not have an airline pilot's licence (ATPL). Indeed, he was a beginner… Given his lack of experience, the young man had the sad privilege of being among the least well-paid crew members in the airline. But money was not his real concern. Like all enthusiasts, he wanted a career in flying and often explained that he was even prepared to work for free or even pay to work in a cockpit. During this flight, he was to be the PNF. He would therefore be dealing with radiocommunications and, as will be seen later, reading the checklists.

The Cabin Crew consisted of four hostesses, their chief being Lourdes Romero Flores. The three young women who worked under her were Sonsoles Lorenzo Simarro, Sonia Rodriguez del Castillo and Susana Marin Ramos. There were also two other hostesses and a steward aboard but they were on their way to start their tour of duty in the Canaries[3] so they were in uniform but not working (deadhead passengers in cabin jargon).

Initially, Spanair transit services announced that there were 163 passengers aboard. This was the figure written on the flight manifest but a few moments before the crew shut the doors, three new passengers turned up. Among these was Fernandez Vasquez, a Captain deadheading to the Canaries to take over a flight there. None of these passengers should have been aboard the DC-9 for they had all been destined to take another flight. But the scheduling services offered them this last minute opportunity and they all seemed happy to embark.
But there are days when it is better not to be lucky!

Following the unexpected arrival of these newcomers, the Captain modified the flight manifest. Taking them and their luggage into account, the aircraft weighed 226 kg more than planned. Its take-off weight would now be exactly 64.528 tons.
One of the late arrivals was Gabriel Guerrero, a steward. As he was an aviation enthusiast, he asked if he could travel inside the cockpit. The Captain granted him permission and he was given the jump seat placed between the pilots' seats. He was delighted to be in this spot because he could watch the instrument panel at leisure.

The DC-9-82 in this story was not exactly a recent aircraft type, since its prototype had made its maiden flight in 1965. Since that date, more than 2,500 of them had been sold and the aircraft had acquired an excellent reputation with airlines. It was reliable and easy to fly. The one in this story was 15 years old at the time of the events. It had been bought second-hand ten years earlier from *Korean Air* which had kept it perfectly maintained. Spanish pilots greatly appreciated this machine which had rendered untold services to Spanair.
The problem was that in this month of August 2008 the DC-9 was no longer the type of aircraft suited to the prevailing economic crisis. In fact, despite its many qualities, it had one enormous fault: its old Pratt & Witney JT8D-219 engines were real fuel guzzlers[4]. Since the beginning of the year, the price of the barrel

[3] Raquel Perez Sanchez, Antonia Martinez Jimenez and Gabriel Guerrero.
[4] The JT8D equipped among others the Boeing 727, 737-200, Mercure and even later versions of the Caravelle.

had skyrocketed and the cost of fuel had had tragic effects on airlines' financial health.

But that was not all. McDonnell-Douglas, the manufacturer of the DC-9, was bought up by Boeing in 1997. The new owner's strategy was simple: eliminate all the old DC-9s from the market and replace them with its own products. Spare parts therefore became expensive and delivery lead-times interminable. In these conditions, it had become extremely difficult to manage a DC-9-equipped fleet.

For Spanair, the financial losses were huge. Although it was the second largest Spanish airline after Iberia, it was on the brink of going out of business. To try and set things right, the management took drastic measures. Fifteen out of its fleet of 36 aircraft were grounded. They decided to lay off a quarter of the staff and closed down a number of routes they thought unprofitable. It was a bitter pill for the staff to swallow... Everybody was expecting to receive a registered letter saying how marvellously competent they were, but also suggesting they seek employment elsewhere. Even the pilots were vulnerable. Closing down routes and grounding aircraft weakened their position considerably. On the same morning as these events occurred, SEPLA, the Spanair airline pilots' union, had decided to go out on strike and the atmosphere within the airline was becoming more strained by the day.

This situation was not the direct cause of the accident about to take place, but it did contribute to it considerably. It had the insidious effect of making the employees feel less concerned about Spanair's future. And experience has shown that when the personnel are not motivated, the consequences can be felt immediately as far as safety is concerned.

The 20 August 2008, the Spanair flight was number JKK 022. As it was on code share with Lufthansa there was a second flight number: LH 2554[5].

---

[5] "Code share" is a commercialisation method between two airlines. One operates the flight, the other commercialises it in part. This explains why the same aircraft can appear under two different numbers on flight information panels.

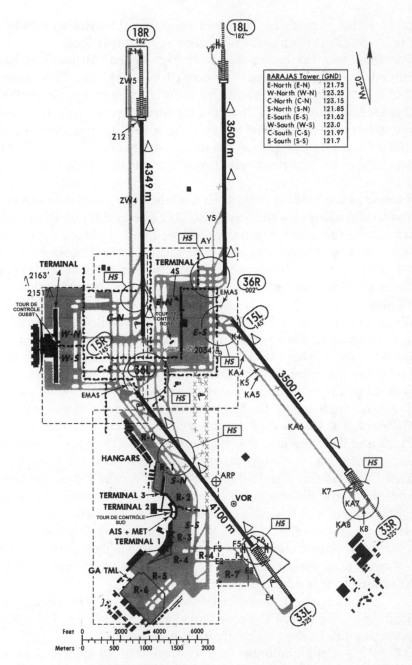

Overall diagram of the four runways and taxiways at Madrid-Barajas.
The points marked HS (Hot Spot) were the "hot" points where pilots had to be
careful not to go onto a runway accidentally.

At **13:13** the aircraft left Terminal 2 and taxied for Runway 36 left, the longest at this airport - more than 4,334 yards long.

The DC-9 was taxiing at relatively high speed. Although it had landed at 10:13 it was now almost 10 minutes late. This meant that it had been on the ground for exactly three hours. Given that the average stopover for low-cost airlines is around 20 minutes, you get an idea of how low Spanair's profitability was. An aircraft that remains on the ground too long costs money; the time factor was to play an important role throughout the events to come.

Taxiing to the holding point took a while. First of all, the aircraft had to taxi alongside runway 15R/33L right to the end then head out among the maze of taxiways Mike 14 and 15. Madrid-Barajas stretches out over a large area. The airport is now ranked 11th in the world and has developed extensively over the last few years. There are three control towers and four runways, two of which are aligned north-south[6].

While taxiing, the crew went through all the checklists and, at first, everything went normally. Nothing was forgotten, especially the wing flaps, which would be deflected through 11 degrees, this being the recommended configuration for this type of take-off. Deflecting the wing flaps automatically caused the slats – lip-like extensions to the leading edge of the wing – to extend (see photograph at the start of this story).

Flaps and the slats are vital high lift devices. They are especially important when the temperature is hot and when the aircraft is heavy (as was the case to-day). Note that, on the DC-9, the flaps and the slats always work simultaneously. Indeed, the pilot controls them with a single lever on the centre console.

Depending on the flight phase, the crew had three choices:

- The flaps could be completely retracted. This configuration is mainly used when cruising. The aircraft does not normally take off or land in this arrangement.

- The flaps could be deflected 14 degrees. This is the maximum used for taking off but the crew can also opt for a lower deflection. Generally the 11 degrees configuration is chosen.

- The flaps could be fully deployed to 40 degrees, as in the photo at the beginning of this text. This is the configuration generally used for landing.

---

[6] See diagram: the four runways are 15L/33R (3,500 m- 2.18 miles), 15R/33L (4,100 m-2.56 miles), 18R/36L (4,349m-2.71 miles) and 18L/33R (3,500 m-2.18 miles).

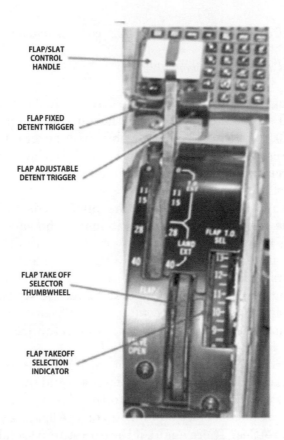

FLAP/SLAT
CONTROL
HANDLE

FLAP FIXED
DETENT TRIGGER

FLAP ADJUSTABLE
DETENT TRIGGER

FLAP TAKE OFF
SELECTOR
THUMBWHEEL

FLAP TAKEOFF
SELECTION
INDICATOR

As the DC-9 was taxiing towards the runway, the crew had extended the flaps by 11 degrees. When it reached Zulu 2 on the side-strip, all the checklists had been completed.

Everything so far was normal. Just an ordinary flight getting ready to take off with a bunch of tourists aboard, including many children. A noisy, festive atmosphere prevailed in the cabin as the passengers were happily looking forward to reaching their paradisiacal holiday destination just three hours away.

At **13:25:03** the Captain asked for clearance to enter the runway. The controller cleared him and, as is customary, asked him to call when he was ready for take-off.
It was from now on that events started to take a more unusual turn. The DC-9 lined up but the seconds ticked by and the crew did not call back.
As no controller likes to see their runway occupied for long, the controller decided to prompt the Captain:

13:26:07 (Controller): *Spanair 5022, call me when you're ready.*

13:26:13 (Captain): *Roger 5022.*

But nothing happened... In fact, the Captain had just noticed that the digital instrument indicating the outside temperature was showing 101 degrees C! As it was obviously never quite so hot in Spain, the crew were trying to fathom what was happening. Was it a short-circuit or a simple indication defect in the gauge?[7] Should they take off in such conditions?

Novices may be wondering why the pilot needs to know what the outside air temperature is. Is it just so he can impress the passengers by announcing that it is -50 °C at altitude?

There are in fact two reasons why this parameter needs to be known. Firstly, it enables the crew to keep an eye on the risk of icing during the flight so they can take corrective action by turning on the anti-icing systems. Secondly, the on-board computer uses the air temperature parameter to manage the thrust from the engines by means of the auto-throttles[8].

What should the crew do? Take off or return to the apron?

They hesitated... No icing zone was forecast and there was not the slightest storm cloud on the route to the Canary Islands So that day there was no risk of ice building up on the leading edges... And the auto-throttles? There again, if the auto-throttles failed to work all they would have to do was operate them manually or indicate the speed manually.

But they just waited, not bothering to call the controller. The aircraft remained at a standstill in the middle of the runway while, slightly behind them, at the holding point, an Iberia Airbus was awaiting its turn.

The crew attempted to analyse the situation. Meanwhile, the temperature indication continued to rise with the gauge now showing 103° C... It was now certain; they had a malfunction, probably the "RAT" probe[9].

---

[7] The instrument is located in the centre of the instrument panel above the engine instruments.

[8] When the auto-throttle system is activated, the thrust levers move by themselves without intervention from the crew and the computer regulates power depending on the aircraft's speed, the required climb or descent rate and the outside temperature.

[9] The Ram Air Temperature probe has the advantage of not taking into account kinetic heating that takes place in contact with the air above 250 mph.

This probe was in the shape of a metal tube fitted to the front right part of the fuselage... Was it really malfunctioning? The fact that it was overheating did not mean it was not working. In fact it was the heater designed to prevent it from icing that was overheating! The Captain hesitated... After all, it would cool down as soon as they took off, except that the probe heater should normally never function by itself when the aircraft is on the ground.

Temperature probe

And things failed to improve... A final glance at the instrument showed that the probe's temperature had now reached 104°C. Examination of the black boxes showed that it had continued to heat up ever since the aircraft had left the apron. At that moment, the crew did not know that the malfunction was due to an electric relay. It was still functioning when it should have been deactivated when the aircraft was on the ground.

Note that this malfunction was nothing new. This was the sixth time in three days that this had occurred and nothing had been done about it[10]. This was symptomatic of the crisis Spanair was going

---

[10] The malfunction was in fact caused by a failure of relay R2-5, which remained permanently connected when it should be disconnect automatically when the aircraft is on the ground.

through; you could sense it was the end of an era, with professional conscientiousness becoming more of a slogan than a reality.
Blocked at the holding point, the Iberia Airbus was still waiting to take the DC-9's place but the crew was still dithering.

Finally the Captain decided he needed more time to think.

13:26:27 (Captain): *5022, we have a technical problem... We cancel our take off for the moment.*

There was silence on the frequency. It was rather rare for a lined up aircraft to issue such a message.

13:26:45 (Controller): *What are you going to do, 5022?*

13:26:52 (Captain hesitating): *Well, we'd like to get off the runway.*

13:26:56 (Controller): *Roger, 5022, next exit on your left.*

The aircraft moved forward a few yards and turned into "Zulu 6". As soon as the runway was free, the Iberia Airbus behind it lined up in its place.
At first, the DC-9 turned left again on ZW1 and halted facing south on heading 185. There it remained for a full seven minutes. This pause tells a lot about the situation. In fact the Captain and the First Officer were in full discussion but were unable to decide whether or not to go back to the gate[11]. The temperature of the probe had now stabilised at 104° C. Returning would mean a considerable loss of time and they were already late... On the other hand, no pilot ever wants to take off with an inoperative system. In the present instance, it was obvious that there was an electrical problem somewhere. A short circuit could start a fire in flight[12].
Finally, after much hesitation, the Captain made the most reasonable decision:

13:33:12 (Captain to Tower): *5022, well... we haven't solved our problem... we wish to return to the parking.*

---

[11] Although the transcript of the conversations was not recovered from the CVR, the information had subsequently been communicated by the First Officer to the two maintenance mechanics.

[12] See the crash of Flight Swissair 111 in "Le Secret des Boites Noires" by the same author.

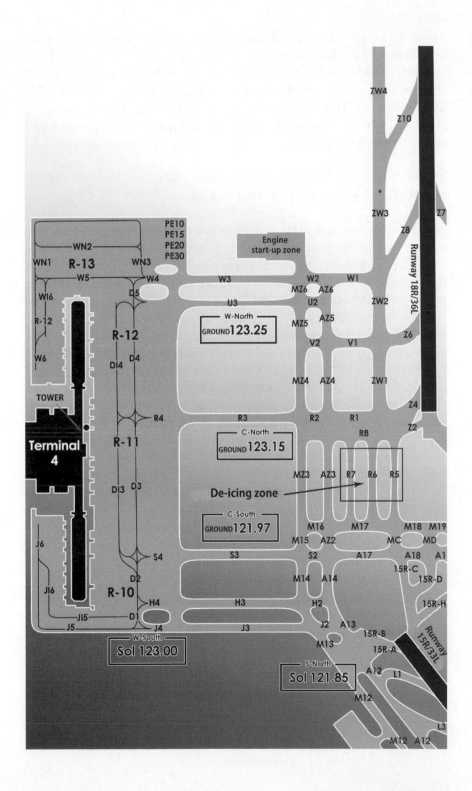

There followed a few seconds of silence... The controller informed his shift supervisor that Flight Spanair 5022 had just been cancelled. Another position on the apron had to be found for it. But this was not so easy as the aircraft could not go back to Gate T21. Meanwhile, another aircraft had taken its place and the passengers were already disembarking. A quick consultation took place in the tower to solve the problem, and then the controller answered:

13:33:47 (Controller): *Copied, Spanair 5022, taxi towards Romeo 11. We'll ask your technical team to join you there.*

The DC-9 continued taxiing slowly towards its new place on the apron, just in front of Terminal 4. It was much closer than Gate T21. This was therefore an advantage because the clock was ticking by. From now on, the crew was to feel divided between its desire to solve the problem and to get going again as quickly as possible.

While the aircraft was taxiing, its flaps were deflected in the 11° take-off configuration and, at first they remained like that. The two men were fully focused on the probe overheating problem and nothing else seemed to concern them. The Captain asked the First Officer to make a brief announcement over the Public Address System to inform the passengers about the situation. He explained over the intercom that they had "a technical problem, nothing serious, just a red light somewhere." Conversations in the cabin ceased at once. The atmosphere became tense. Even if the words "not serious" had been pronounced, everybody was puzzled.

It was **13:39** when the DC-9 reached Romeo 11. A gangway was already in place to meet it. It was only then that the Captain at last raised the flaps... The APU[13] was switched off and so there was no longer any air conditioning.
Everything went quickly. Everybody was aware that the time factor was vital because the passengers could not be left for long in such sweltering conditions. As soon as the gangway was set up a ground staff member and two Spanair technicians were at the door. The steward got up from his jump seat and the Captain had them come into the cockpit. There was no need to be a specialist to understand the problem. All you had to do was glance at the RAT temperature indicator diodes on the top of the instrument panel to

---

[13] Auxiliary Power Unit: a small turbine that backs up the on-board batteries by providing the electrical power supply on the ground

see that the probe was overheating. It was still at 104 degrees C. The technicians however were reassuring. One of them explained that "of course it was overheating, but that as soon as the aircraft got airborne, the air flow would cool the probe down and everything would be back to normal. It should be possible for you to leave like that".

At first Captain Garcia Luna seemed to disagree.

During this ongoing discussion, a number of people came and went from the cockpit. The steward Gabriel Guerrero left to wait in the front galley. José Fernandez Vazquez, the other Spanair Captain now appeared to enquire what was going on. A technician gave him the lowdown. Lourdes Flores then appeared, wanting to know what to tell the passengers as they were intent on knowing what the problem was... In the middle of all this disorder the technicians gave their opinion. Some of their suggestions were decidedly odd. One of them even suggested they cool the probe with dry ice. That would be easy because there was a large stock at the airport[14]. Quite obviously they would need a ladder to reach the probe on the side of the fuselage but it should work... The mind boggles at such a strange idea - how on earth would cooling down the probe solve the electrical problem?

Naturally Captain Garcia Luna disagreed with this new suggestion and reminded them that they had been informed about the problem several days beforehand - and of course nothing had been done about it. He demanded that the problem be settled immediately and as nobody seemed to be taking his request seriously he ended up losing his temper.

13:51:48 (Captain testily): *I'm telling you, we're wasting a lot of time here, and I'm going to make a report on what's going on.*

At the same moment, the first clamours of protest from the passengers could be heard coming from the cabin. Some of them were complaining of the heat. Everybody understood the aircraft had a breakdown and a sense of fear was wriggling its way into people's minds. The First Officer's talk about a red light had not reassured anybody. The technicians going in and out of cockpit added to the stress.

---

[14] Dry ice is carbon dioxide (CO_2) in solid form. Its sublimation temperature is in the region of -78°. When in contact with water, this product is often used in shows to imitate smoke or fog.

A stocky Spanish passenger suddenly got up and, adopting a rather aggressive attitude, drew attention to the fact that there were a lot of children on board and that they could not be left in this situation forever.

The hostess explained very calmly they had encountered a minor incident of no real consequence. Another passenger wanted to know if there was a problem with the engines. The stewardess replied that she did not know but that she would find out. So she headed for the cockpit but did not come back.

The protests quickly mounted in intensity. Some passengers could be heard saying they wanted to leave the aircraft. So the Cabin Senior Lourdes Romero returned to explain that that was quite impossible. Now that they were aboard the aircraft, it would be too impractical for them to disembark as the luggage would have to be recovered from the cargo compartment, the manifest modified, the security formalities gone through again... This failed to convince many of the passengers as they were on a domestic flight and there were no administrative formalities to be dealt with[15].

Sitting in seat 6C, Kim Tate Perez phoned her mother to tell her she had had enough. "It's terribly hot and they're an hour and a half late". Kim was an English music teacher who had chosen to take Spanish nationality when she married. She was going back home to the Canary Islands after two weeks holiday in Bulgaria and she had never imagined that a trip could be so complicated. She explained to her mother that "the aircraft seemed to have a failure. It had been about to take off and then the pilot had cancelled it." She said she was frightened.

Next to her in Seat 6C was a small girl called Maria Alvarez Carretero travelling with her younger brother Ricardo. He was sitting next to the window. Both of them were also very hot. Kim Tate carried on talking to her mother at length. She said "that some people had asked to leave the aircraft but the hostesses refused".

At the same moment another passenger, Ruben Santana, sent an SMS to his wife Maria to tell her that he had just asked to leave the aircraft but this had been refused. When his wife called back, he explained that "some passengers heard they were going to change aircraft".

---

[15] The Canary Islands are in the Atlantic Ocean just off Morocco but form an integral part of Spanish territory. Although 1,250 miles away, the flight was a domestic one with no border crossing.

All this fuss could only tarnish the airline's image and ground management were worried. In the stopover office, the airline's Operations Manager and the airport Operations Manager were discussing whether or not to replace the aircraft. This conversation was reported after the accident and evidently aroused a great deal of controversy.

Airport management insisted on being kept informed at once as to the airline's decision as the DC-9 was not in a suitable parking area. If it was going to stay in Madrid, it would have to move. As things became tenser, they called the control tower to confirm that they would have to delay the flight plan for another hour, but they also added that there was also a risk of it simply being cancelled. The debated continued in the cockpit.

13:53:21 (Captain addressing a hostess): *How are things in the cabin? Aren't they too hot?*

13:53:48 (Hostess): *Yes, there's a problem, Captain. They're complaining and they want to know what's going to happen.*

Next to the cockpit, the technicians continued to palaver. They had no idea as to how to resolve the matter as they did not have any wiring diagrams. How could they repair anything in such conditions? It would take time. The passengers could be heard protesting. They would have to be disembarked... and all this due to a faulty temperature probe. In the end the technical supervisor found a solution that seemed to satisfy everybody. All they needed to do was pull the "breaker" (basically a fuse just like domestic ones). All aircraft have several dozens of them, each of which applies to a particular item of equipment. Pulling the probe's circuit breaker would not fix things but the problem could be ignored. This was a strange way of reasoning since it was not the de-icing system that had broken down and it was actually the probe that was overheating, but working all the time. Time went by... The technicians failed to investigate any further and did not realise that the problem was elsewhere, on relay R2-5, which was no longer operational. This faulty relay would lead to dire consequences.

When the Captain was asked what he thought about pulling the breaker, he answered:

13:53:54: *Yes, we ought to be able to go like that. There's no icing forecast on the route.*

13:54:00 (MT3 Technician): *I agree... We'll give you the aircraft back with the probe heater de-activated.*

The technical supervisor pulled lightly on the breaker marked "RAT Probe and Heater"[16]. There was a dry click and the probe's electrical circuit was disconnected.
The technical supervisor at once expressed his satisfaction at having "solved the problem".

13:55:04 (MT3 Technician): *You see, everything's okay now!*

All that had to be done now was fill in the paperwork to certify the "repairs". An airliner cannot take off just like that when a system is not functioning properly. The crew has to check first that the malfunction does not go against the MEL[17]. The MEL gives a precise list of the breakdowns that can and cannot be tolerated when an aircraft is about to take off. It would be inconceivable, for example, to let an aircraft leave with an engine failure. But keeping it grounded because of a broken light bulb in the cockpit would be absurd. The list also takes into account other operational factors such as what spare parts are available on the spot and how much time the repair would take. Taking into account all these factors, the MEL can be used to apply a temporary concession and allow an aircraft to take off with a minor malfunction. But in no event must this relaxation have any detrimental effect on safety; it is only resorted to as an exception and cannot be renewed indefinitely without the repair being carried out.

Having checked that the probe heater malfunction was clearly provided for in the MEL, the Captain and the technical supervisor both signed the document. The DC-9 could leave.

Time to move on. No problem any more!

Unfortunately there *was* a problem. When he pulled the breaker, the technician did not eliminate the *reason* for the malfunction. Had he pursued his reasoning, he would have grasped the fact that

---

[16] Reheat and Temperature Probe.
[17] Minimum Equipment List.

the probe was not defective (this was clear since it was overheating) and discovered that it was Relay R2-5 that was malfunctioning. And that gave rise to another and much more dangerous issue: *the take-off configuration alarm was not working ...*

This alarm, known as the "TOWS"[18], is fitted to all airliners and is a kind of call to order when something has been forgotten just before take-off, similar to the beep signal in cars when a driver forgets to put their seat belt on, or if the parking brake is still applied.

On a DC-9, there are five reasons for the computer to warn the crew if the aircraft is not ready for take-off:

- The park brake is still on (as on a car!)
- The auto brake system has not been selected[19].
- The speed brakes are deployed.
- The trim is badly set.
- And finally... *when the flaps are not in the take-off position.*

These points are all vital. A single oversight can jeopardise the aircraft's safety. The TOWS is a hooter coupled to an artificial voice that clearly announces what has been forgotten. But that day, since the R2-5 relay had broken down, this alarm was not functioning... and the crew had no idea of the situation. Their only concern for the time being was to catch up on lost time. The delay even appears to have caused problems of a strictly personal nature. Thus, despite the tense situation, the First Officer, Javier Mulet, warned his girlfriend that he would not be back on time that evening:

13:54:47 (First Officer talking with a friend on his cell phone): *It's me, listen... I'm still in Madrid... we've been delayed, I can't do anything about it. I'll be back late. We'll have to change our plans for this evening.*

While the young man was apologising to his girl friend, the Captain, Garcia Luna, finished filling in the MEL form with the technicians. He confirmed to the Operations Manager that he had agreed to take off without the temperature probe and its heater and sought to justify his decision by repeating that no ice zone was forecast on the route and there was therefore no risk...

---

[18] Take Off Warning System. Also called Take Off Configuration on some aircraft.

[19] The DC-9 is one of the rare aircraft on which forgetting the auto-brake sets off the TOWS. On other aircraft, this equipment must not be used when power is increased.

Once the papers had been signed, he addressed the First Officer:

14:02:36 (Captain): *I'm going down while they're refuelling. Inform the passengers...*

It has already been seen that the DC-9 consumes a lot of fuel. So, during the few minutes the aircraft taxied through the airport, its engines had guzzled 880 lb. The Captain was keen to avoid any further risks and wanted to fill up so as to leave with full tanks. But since the passengers were still aboard, he first had to warn them and instruct them to unfasten their seat belts so they could evacuate if a fire broke out... And as they were late, the Captain went down onto the tarmac to hurry things up.
Hurry up! From then on, the crew were obsessed with caching up on lost time and everything was a rush.
Unfortunately, in aeronautics, "haste" never rhymes with "safety".

At **14:06** Garcia Luna returned to his seat. Before entering the cockpit, he asked the Cabin Senior to have the gangway pulled away and to close the door behind him.
The steward Gabriel Guerrero unfolded the jump-seat and unobtrusively took his place again in the centre of the cockpit. He was keen not to disturb the crew so they could get on with the tasks in hand. Things went quickly... Garcia Luna had not even fastened his harness before he instructed Javier Mulet to call the control tower and request start up clearance.
The First Officer obeyed immediately.

14:07:02 (First Officer): *Barajas hello, Spanair 5022, we request start up for Gran Canaria[20].*

However, in his haste the First Officer had just made a first mistake. He called on the frequency to which his radio had originally been set at 123.25 MHz... This was the ground frequency for taxiing. The controller replied irritably as the DC-9's problems had created a certain amount of confusion at the airport and the atmosphere was tense.

14:07:20 (Ground Frequency Controller): *Spanair 5022, call Clearance Delivery on 130.07...*

---

[20] For an ILR flight plan, the engines can only be started up on authorisation from air control.

Cursing himself, the First Officer switched over to the correct frequency.

14:07:52 (First Officer): *Barajas from Spanair 5022, requesting start up please.*

14:08:08 (Controller): *You are cleared to start up 5022. Call ready for taxi.*

The First Officer just had time to put his microphone down before starting to read the "Pre-start checklist". It would be practically impossible for crew members to remember by heart all the checks that have to be made so they always resort to the written procedures corresponding to each particular phase of the flight.

Looking at the table below, it can be seen that the first "Pre-start check" checklist is a long one with its 26 items. Under normal circumstances, this takes some time. Here the pilot took exactly 7 seconds to read through the whole list. This was not the airplane's first flight of the day for which there were some 59 points to be checked. But even so! He reeled off the items at top speed, almost mechanically and often incomprehensibly.

The two men then started on the second list, the "Before Start Up Checklist". This too was covered in record time and, worse still, when the investigators listened to the recording, they realised that the Captain was anticipating the actions even before the First Officer had finished announcing them. Thus, he had not finished pronouncing the words "seat belts", "close doors" "anti-collision", or "report from the cabin" before the Captain had gone onto something else.

The crew had just one overriding idea – that of getting away as quickly as possible.

Before resuming the account of events it might be useful to take a closer look at aircraft checklists. There are five of these to be gone through before each departure. Airline procedures require the First Officer to read the checklist and the Captain to respond and act where necessary.

CHECKLIST NAME	NUMBER OF ITEMS
Pre-start	59 (first flight of the day) 26 (if one of the pilots remained aboard during the stopover)
Before start-up	8
After start-up	9
Taxiing	12
Take-off imminent	6

As can be seen from the above table, some of the checklists contain a considerable number of items[21]. This is normal for older generation aircraft like the DC-9 whereas for modern airplanes like the more recent Airbus models many of these checks are fully or partially handled by the electronics. Here, it was up to the crew to make sure that everything was functioning properly.

The procedure also states that when the First Officer comes to the end of a check-list, he is obliged to state "Checklist completed" before going on do to anything else.

So a check-list is both precise and time consuming – frustratingly so when you are in a hurry.

At **14:09:01**, the crew started the first engine. While watching the engine RPM rise, Garcia Luna and Javier Mulet wondered whether they should proceed with a manual take-off or use the auto-throttles, but disagreed on the matter. The First Officer thought that the auto-throttles would not work since the temperature probe was down, but the Captain was uncertain.

Exchanges between the two men continued apace, indicative of their growing edginess. One can imagine the Captain's state of mind, blaming himself for the delay. After all, he could have pulled the breaker out of the probe himself and there would have

---

[21] The number of items on the checklist varies according to the type of aircraft and also, even for the same type, according to the different electronics options chosen by the airline.

been no need to call in the technicians. Their late departure would now have repercussions on the whole turnaround and the day was going to be a long one. Having left Barcelona in the morning they had now been in Madrid for more than four hours and the Canary Islands were a further three hours away. The aircraft then had to return to Barcelona that same night.

Clearly, the incident had not put the crew in the best state of mind to concentrate fully on the take-off.

The second engine had barely stabilised before the crew started the third checklist, "After start up". It was now that the fateful decision was made. As before, the First Officer went through the list of items at top speed but as he reached the last line, the Captain interrupted him abruptly:

14:12:08 (Captain): *Request taxi straightaway!*

This last item (N° 9) that had been missed out from the checklist concerned the flaps. The First Officer should have asked:
"Flaps and slats?
And the Captain should have answered:
"Set and checked"
So the flaps were not extended at that time. Maybe the First Officer thought he could resume his reading after having contacted the tower but we shall never know. For the time being he put his procedures manual aside and took up his microphone:

14:12:09 (First Officer): *Madrid Spanair 5022, we've started up, we are ready for taxi.*

The controller's reply must have been extremely frustrating:

14:12:20 (Ground Control): *Standby, I'll call you, 5022.*

But he failed to do so... Time went by and there was silence on the flight deck. The steward sat passively observing events. Did the First Officer think at that moment of resuming the unfinished checklists? Apparently not... Finally, Captain Garcia Luna got tired of waiting and seized the microphone to contact the controller, barely hiding his growing irritation:

14:14:23 (Captain): *Barajas, can you tell us how much longer we're going to have to wait?*

This time, the request was successful and just ten seconds elapsed before the controller answered:

14:14:33 (Ground Control): *Spanair 5022, you are cleared to taxi for runway 36 left... Report reaching holding point.*

Acknowledging the instructions, the Captain released the park brake and the aircraft immediately started taxiing[22]. In all, fixing the probe had taken 33 minutes...

As soon as the aircraft got under way, the First Officer started reading the fourth checklist ("Taxi"), seemingly oblivious to the fact that the last item on the third list had been omitted. Once again, he announced each item rapidly and the Captain's answers were just as mechanical as before and the same oversight was repeated. Things were going so fast that at no time did either of the two men once mention the word "flaps". Here too it appeared last on the list and once again it was missed out and at that moment the flaps were therefore still at zero.

And that is how they stayed!

The aircraft was moving quickly along taxiway Mike 15, then Mike 16 followed by Mike 17 before heading towards Romeo 5, the same spot where it had occupied on its first take-off attempt.

At **14:16:50**, the First Officer switched to the tower's frequency: 187.07 MHz.

As the aircraft advanced, they continued discussing whether the auto-throttles would work or not. The Captain thought they would but the First Officer was still convinced of the contrary and was insistent:

14:18:14 (First Officer): *Auto-throttles won't work without the outside temperature.*

He was something of a novice but not so badly informed! In reality, the fact that the levers did not work would not have been a problem. If they did not move by themselves they would have to be moved manually.

---

[22] Once the brakes are released, the thrust can be set by pushing the levers manually or by pressing the TOGA switch and, in that case, the levers function by themselves without the crew having to intervene.

At **14:18:58**, the DC-9 reached Romeo 5 and came to a halt. An aircraft was already on the runway waiting for clearance to take off. At last, it got clearance and took off and the controller called.

14:21:05 (Tower): *Spanair 5022, cleared for line up Runway 36 left and hold.*

14:22:06: Two chimes echoed in the cockpit. This was the pre-arranged signal from the Cabin Senior saying the passengers and the cabin were ready for take-off

The aircraft turned slowly to the right and entered Zulu 2. At present the runway threshold was just a few yards away... Take off was imminent. Now was the time to carry out the final "Take-off Imminent" checklist comprising the last six items before departure, the very last of which is to check the flaps.

TAKE-OFF IMMINENT CHECKLIST	
Spoilers	entered
Take-off parameters	V1 – VR – V2 checked
Lights	on
Flight instruments	checked
Engine instruments	checked
Flaps 11 degrees	checked

The DC-9's last checklist

The First Officer grasped the plastic-covered sheet and started to read it just as he had done for the others. As he finished the checklist, incredibly he came out with the following:

14:22:15 (First Officer): *And last item... we have... 8... sorry... 11... retracted... 11... retracted...*

before concluding in a tone that brooked no contradiction:

14:22:31 (First Officer): *Checklist completed...*

This was staggering! The young man had just alluded to the flaps, first stating they were lowered to 8 degrees, then 11 degrees, then retracted, then 11 degrees again before finally stating they were retracted. This was incomprehensible! The whole series of contradictory statements showed that the First Officer did not take the time to think things out. The words were pronounced automatically and seem not correspond to any conscious through processes. His mind was clearly elsewhere. This nonsense would be comical if it had not had such a dramatic impact on 176 people's lives.

This last item seemed so unimportant to the First Officer that he went straight onto another matter asking the Captain, in the second that followed, if he wanted to put the Autopilot on once they had taken off.

The Captain did not respond.

The controller finally issued the long-awaited clearance a few seconds later.

14:23:09 (Controller): *Clear for take-off Runway 36 left Spanair 5022... Wind 220 for 7 knots.*

The First Officer acknowledged this message. At this moment there were 4,756 yards of cement in front of the aircraft. It is one of Europe's longest runways and therefore one of the safest. Moreover, there was nothing especially dangerous about today's take-off. All it needed now was for the plane to take off at the correct speed as corresponding to the 11° flap setting. On that day, that speed was high because the aircraft was practically at its maximum take-off weight[23]and the weather was hot.

One second later the Captain pushed both throttle levers forward. The brakes were released and the aircraft started to accelerate. The engine data were normal but as the pilot had predicted, the auto-throttles did not work but, more seriously, when he pushed the throttles forward, no alarm sounded.

Now, as we have seen, an alarm should have sounded as the flaps were not extended. The take off configuration alarm should have warned the crew that something was amiss.

But nothing happened. No hooter... No synthetic voice. As relay

---

[23] The maximum take-off weight is 66.6 tons. Here, the aircraft weighed 64.5 tons.

R2-5 was faulty, there was no alarm.

Convinced that everything was alright, the crew continued its take off in blessed ignorance.

The aircraft continued to accelerate without difficulty... Outside the heat reflecting off the hot tarmac further increased the ambient air temperature that was now 32° C (although the crew did not know this since the probe had been deactivated).

As was the procedure, the First Officer called out that the aircraft was reaching 60 knots.

Then he called 100 knots.

The aircraft continued to accelerate. Engine thrust was nominal. The EPR was 1.95.

A few moments earlier, the crew had worked out that the V1 decision speed was 154 knots[24]. But this speed had been calculated with the flaps extended at 11°. And they were at zero!

14:24:05 (First Officer): *V1...*

They had gone past the decision speed. From now on, it was no longer possible to stop. They were past the point of no return. Whatever happened they would have to take off.

14:24:09 (First Officer): *Rotation.*

Apparently everything was normal. The Captain exerted pressure on the stick and pulled back firmly... One second later the nose wheel lifted off and the electronic system went over from the "on ground" mode to the "in flight" mode. Then the main landing gear left the ground.

The aircraft was airborne. It was **14:24:10** and the aircraft had covered 2,123 yards since release of the brakes, not yet even half the runway length but they were beyond the point of no return.

Calmly the Captain adopted the normal 15.5 degrees pitch attitude. It was now that things started to go wrong. The aircraft was only 25 feet off the ground when the stick shaker was triggered. This is an alarm that warns the pilot that his aircraft is about to stall. The system is designed to make the control column vibrate unpleasantly, the aim being to discourage the pilot from pulling back on the stick. He had to decrease the angle of attack. But it was already too late. The aircraft veered off onto its right wing. At first it banked by 4.4°. The First Officer started shouting:

---

[24] 60 knots= 69 mph, 100 knots = 115 mph 154 knots for V1= 178 mph.

14:24:14 (First Officer): *We have an engine failure!*

He was mistaken... both engines were at full power and without the slightest fault. The problem was that there was not enough speed/lift to enable the aircraft to fly properly. The DC-9 was several feet off the ground but it was unstable. It was veering to the right and vibrating violently. Then the bank increased going abruptly to 20 degrees. The Captain reacted and pulled the stick to the left to counter the movement but in doing so increased the aircraft's instability. Worse was to come... surprised by the aircraft banking abruptly, he had just made the wrong move. For one second the throttles were reduced, the result being that engine power fell to 1.65 EPR. This blunder only lasted one second since the levers were pushed back to the full position at once... The EPR increased to 2.15 but unfortunately it wasn't enough to restore the situation.

It was now too late; the aircraft had become uncontrollable.
The stick shaker continued. Other alarms were set off. The stall warning screamed:

14:24:15 (Synthetic voice with hooter): *Stall... Stall... Stall.*

The Captain's angry response was incongruous:

14:24:17 (Captain): *God, how can we get that voice to shut up?*

At the same time, the EGPWS[25] sounded. The system was set off because the aircraft was getting close to the ground and out of control. The synthetic voice gave another warning to the crew that the bank angle was too steep. The bank to the right increased. Now the DC-9 had quit the runway. It was still within the airport perimeter but was ploughing through scrubland scattered here and there with dry bushes and thickets.
At **14:24:19** the Captain reacted but made the wrong decision. Frightened by the brutal reaction of his aircraft, he pulled back even harder on the stick. The pitch attitude reached 18.3 degrees... The plane was nose up but not climbing. Although its speed was 168 knots, it began to fall back. The DC-9 was 40 feet off the ground with its nose pointing up to the sky but it was going back down.
To the front of the cabin, Ligia Palomino was sitting in the fifth row. She felt her seat starting to vibrate violently. In fact the

---

[25] Enhanced Ground Proximity Warning.

whole aircraft itself was vibrating. It was swinging from right to left. The sensation was so frightening she could not hold back from screaming.

Then there was suddenly no lift from the wings. Aerodynamic laws no longer applied and the plane became a 65-ton mass attracted by the Earth's gravity.

The aircraft stalled.

Five seconds later, it hit the ground at a speed of 176 mph. The right wing touched first and then the fuselage slammed down. The impact took place with a vertical acceleration of 3.17 g and the aircraft broke in two just behind the flight deck. The fuel tanks burst open, a huge fireball surged forth and the flames spread to the vegetation all around the airport, starting a bush fire.

However, as sometimes happens in this kind of tragedy, there was a miracle. The music teacher, Kim Tate, was one of the rare passengers whose hour had not yet come. She was seated in the sixth row and this was a stroke of luck as it was there that the aircraft broke in two. Kim was then literally ejected from the careering mass of the aircraft and fell into a tiny pond, out of range of the first flames. She hit the ground at more than 153 mph. The rescue teams found her unconscious, still attached to her seat. One of her arms was broken and she had a punctured lung but she had no burns.

The catastrophe caused 153 fatalities among whom 22 were children. One seriously injured man died three days after the accident. Some passengers had been completely burnt and it took several weeks for the bodies to be identified.

Unexpectedly, there were 18 survivors. They had all been sitting near the sixth row. Thus, Ligia Palomino survived. Roberto Alvarez Carretero, the little boy near the window also survived, but his little sister Maria was not so lucky... As for the crew, all were killed in the accident, except for Antonia Martinez Jiminez, one of the deadheading hostesses. She was also in the front of the aircraft.

The first theories published in the media suggested an engine failure. A number of witnesses claimed to have seen flames escaping from the right hand engine. At first, everybody believed this. It fitted in with the scenario that had taken place before take-off. The aircraft had come back to the apron due to the first failure and had been incorrectly repaired. An anonymous Spanair employee even claimed that the engine had shown signs of weakness for several weeks prior to the event.

A video film taken while the aircraft was taking off proved that these witness accounts were unreliable. No flames or even smoke were seen to emerge from the engines[26].

The day after the catastrophe, José Maria Vazquez Alvarez, President of the Spanair pilots' union held a press conference. He claimed the aircraft had been serviced normally and that there were no technical issues. He declared in particular that "attributing the responsibility for the accident to the financial difficulties of the airline was an aberration." This did not prevent certain specialists from criticising the age of the DC-9s and the problems encountered carrying out the repairs.

Faced with these accusations, Spanair quickly published a press release to confirm that it would continue to use and trust its DC-9 fleet. "They are solid and proven aircraft". The spokesman explained that the aircraft in the accident had indeed been delayed by a temperature probe breaking down but that "this had absolutely nothing to do with the catastrophe". He confirmed that the crew was perfectly within its rights to take off without this probe. Which was true.

It did not take the investigators long to discover the real reasons for the disaster. In a preliminary report, they listed three of them:
- The crew forgot to set the flaps.
- The take-off configuration alarm had failed.
- Both men were in a great hurry, causing them to botch the checklists. Reading the procedures correctly would indeed have enabled the oversight to be corrected.

As usual, they noted that a crash is not caused by any single factor. It takes place when a certain number of risk parameters converge at a single point. In the Madrid case, all that was needed was for one of the above reasons to be rectified and the catastrophe would never have occurred.

In its defence, the airline claimed that its maintenance computers had been infected by a Trojan horse type virus revenge attack that had prevented the computers from making a diagnosis of the relay R2-5 failure quickly enough. To check out the truth of these claims,

---

[26] You can see this video on youtube at http://www.youtube.com/watch?v= EA3Qs30iRmc&NR=1

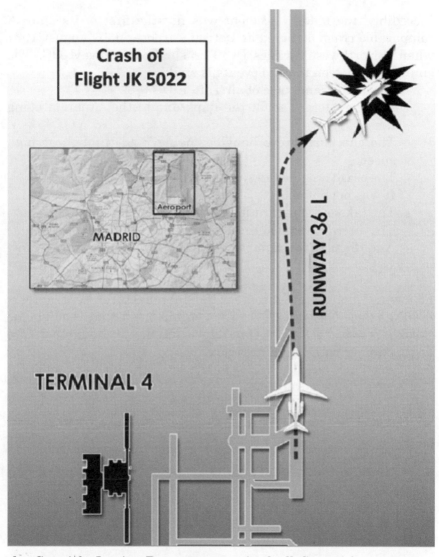

Crash of Flight JK 5022

MADRID — Aeroport

TERMINAL 4

RUNWAY 36 L

the Spanish Justice Department seized all Spanair's computers but nothing came of it. In all events, the mistakes made that day had nothing to do with information technology problems but were all a series of failures relating to the human factor.

Following on from this accident, Spanair's economic difficulties were compounded exponentially. The airline's customers turned to the competition and it was entirely re-organised by new investors. At the time of writing these lines, the financial problems seem to have been solved and Spanair has once again become Spain's second airline. As for the DC-9s, most of them have been replaced by Airbuses.

Incredibly, the Madrid accident was not the first of its kind. A comparable crash occurred at Detroit Airport on 16 August 1987 when a Northwest Airlines DC-9 crashed on Runway 03C. The similarity between the two events is striking:
- It was the same type of aircraft: a DC-9-82.
- The crew forgot about the flaps due to the situation being tense.
- The checklists were bungled, being read through at high speed
- The crash occurred in August.
- It was hot outside.
- The take-off configuration alarm had broken down.
- The aircraft weighed the same on take-off at 65 tons.
- And, finally, the number of victims was exactly the same: 154.

Following the Detroit disaster, the manufacturer sent a telex to all airlines operating DC-9s to remind them that reading the checklists was a vital safety procedure and that it should therefore be carried out with the utmost care.
Apparently the message failed to reach all the airlines, unless it had been forgotten over time.

TUPOLEV IN A FLAT SPIN

Loss of situation awareness

4 July 2001

The Tupolev 154M belonged to the Russian airline "Vladivostok Avia". It was an old tri-jet design of which more than a thousand examples were built. During the Soviet era, it was one of the models most commonly used by the big Eastern bloc airlines. Even though it did not have identical performance, the Tupolev 154 was roughly a copy of the American Boeing 727: the same familiar silhouette with a third engine on the tail, the same passenger capacity and the same characteristic T-tail.
The one referred to here was 15 years old. At the time of the events, it had clocked up 21,000 flying hours. Not that much for an airliner.

The Tupolev 154 M in this story (Registration RA-85845)

That evening the aircraft was doing the night flight between Yekaterinburg and Vladivostok. It was a long haul from Central Russia to the shores of the Sea of Japan during which the aircraft flew over China for almost 936 miles. It was flight XF 352, but rather strangely, the crew never used this number during their various radio contacts with the controllers. Unusually for a regular flight, the Captain just gave the aircraft's registration: RA 85845. This radio procedure was generally reserved for small private aircraft. Later, in the transcript of the conversation it will be seen that the number was even limited to the last three figures: "845". It is 3,187 miles from Yekaterinburg to Vladivostok. As the

Tupolev's range was too short to cover such a distance, a stopover to refuel was scheduled at Irkutsk in Siberia. This would be at around two o'clock in the morning at a completely deserted airport. It was a technical stopover only and the passengers were to remain on board with nobody getting on. Although the three Soloviev D-30KUs were very powerful turbofans, technologically they were quite ancient and extremely thirsty.

Due to the night-time stopover in Irkutsk, the trip between Yekaterinburg and Vladivostok took eight and a half hours.

Generally speaking, the Tupolev 154 was not exactly what you would call the most modern aircraft in the aircraft world but neither was it very old since its first flight had taken place in 1968. However, since then it had barely evolved[1]. It had modern cathode screens and no systems computerisation. Its aerodynamics were "prehistoric" as compared with those of present day aircraft[2].

It was on the flight deck in particular that you could see how behind the times the Russians were technologically. The instrument panel was a depressing green and still comprised a multitude of round analogue instruments. Everything was complex and lacked any form of ergonomics to make it easier for the crews. Indeed, the aircraft was so special to fly that it still needed a four-man crew. So, that evening there were a Captain, First Officer, Flight Engineer and Navigator in the cockpit.

And everyone had their work cut out. One typical detail was that on flight XF 352, thé flight crew outnumbered the hostesses. There were only three of them in the cabin to look after the passengers. The Tupolev was something of a "big flying truck", very uncomfortable but as solid as a rock. It could land on unprepared earthen runways and stay grounded under snow for weeks with only the need for a minimum of maintenance.

---

[1] By comparison, the Boeing 737 flew for the first time in 1967 but there is absolutely nothing in common between the first 737s and 737-900s now flying.

[2] In the days of the Cold War, NATO assigned a somewhat surprising code name to the Tu 154 a: Careless.

The Tupolev 154 instrument panel
Note the analogue instruments, unprotected cables and old fashioned radar
where the pilot had to use an eyepiece to see the screen.

This was Russian style construction: rugged, heavy and reputedly unbreakable. Over the years, this legendary robustness had unfortunately become more of a disadvantage. Indeed, the aircraft was so solid that airlines paid scant attention to servicing it. Why bother changing certain parts when they never broke down since servicing costs money and grounds the aircraft for too long. An aircraft on the ground costs much more than one in the air.

Alas, nothing is indestructible. Even the most robust machines finally disintegrate. The upshot of all this was that with time, the Tupolev 154s had become dangerous. Due to lack of proper servicing, some of them had even exploded in flight, lost their tails or caught fire on landing. This airplane's final record included many casualties. The harsh statistics at the time of writing indicate that the Tupolev 154 has caused exactly 2,739 deaths[3]. Among them was Polish president Lech Kaczynski together with a number of members of his government[4].

Even the Russians, who were pretty hardened to the ups and downs of air transport, were beginning to be wary as the Tu 154

---

[3] Source: Aviation Safety Network.
[4] Read **PILOT ERRORS volume 4** by the same author, published by Editions Altipresse

could turn out to be fickle at the most unexpected moments. Thus, at Sugurt in Siberia on 1 January 2011, a Kogalymavia airline Tu 154 caught fire on the ground as the crew started the engines on the edge of the runway. The Tu 154 was so thirsty that companies tried to save fuel by all means possible, even resorting to the weird solution of having the aircraft towed along the taxiway to the runway by a tractor once all the passengers were aboard. Only when the control tower gave the aircraft clearance to line up did the crew start the engines. Nothing like this occurred in the West but it enabled the companies to save dozens of tons of fuel a year. Following this accident, the Russian authorities envisaged grounding all Tupolev 154s. Unfortunately, this was wishful thinking for the time being since there was no equivalent replacement for some airlines. Despite all its defects, the aircraft was fast and there was nothing else on the second-hand market that was cheaper and in the same category[5].

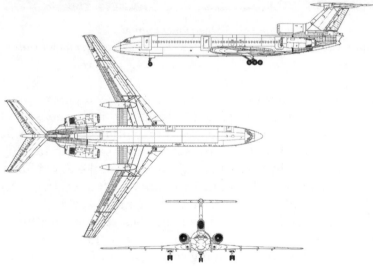

The Tupolev 154

Given these characteristics, it is understandable why it was no easy task to fly a Tupolev 154. This was a machine designed when the Soviet bloc was powerful, a period where the individual was considered almost negligible. Unlike western aircraft that are built around the pilot, Soviet aircraft put men at the controls because it was impossible to do otherwise. But nothing was designed to make

---

[5] You can purchase a Tupolev 154 with a bit of flying potential for 100,000 Euros.

it easier for them. The aircraft was complex, heavy to handle and could not be flown by a single crew member. In the days of the USSR, a single person was not allowed to fly the aircraft in case he fled to the West. Some military versions required up to five crew members.

Flight Engineer's instrument panel (located to the right, behind the First Officer). Note an unusual detail for an airliner: the man has his own throttle levers for all three engines.

Vladivostok Avia is the main private airline in Eastern Russia. At the time of the accident, it was using 24 airliners but it also owned Antonov cargo aircraft and 23 helicopters. Its main destinations were China, Korea and the Far-East in general.

That evening, Flight XF 352 was officially carrying 133 passengers and crew. Among the passengers there were 6 children and 12 Chinese nationals. In reality, there were probably five more people not included on the manifest. Indeed, passengers frequently climbed aboard without a ticket. They were often employees flying free but there could also be friends of the crew and people turned a blind eye[6]. There were even last-minute passengers who had not had time to buy a ticket and were allowed on board in consideration of

---

[6] In most airlines, anybody aboard an aircraft must be either a working member of the crew, a crew member on their way to work, or a ticket holder. Airline employees travelling free must still have a ticket.

a few thousand roubles slipped discreetly into the palm of a hand. This practice was all the more widespread in that the Vladivostok trip cost 20,500 roubles[7]. This was not exactly cheap for the average Russian whose purchasing power had shrunk drastically since the demise of the Soviet Union in the nineties. This did not prevent the airline from expanding because the land route is obviously so much longer: the famous Trans-Siberian railway takes a whole week to reach Vladivostok from Moscow.

As was often the case, Flight XF 352 also carried a certain number of military personnel. Vladivostok is Russia's biggest east coast naval base and a fair share of its clientele were sailors on leave, passengers not renowned for their impeccable behaviour. Just reading the instructions the airline hands out to its passengers gives an idea of the general atmosphere. The website indicates that apart from smoking and drinking alcohol being forbidden aboard the aircraft, passengers are not allowed to:

- pester their neighbour,
- raise their voices aggressively against the Captain or crew members,
- use safety equipment without being first ordered to do so by the Captain or crew.

Even more surprisingly it is strictly forbidden to:

- carry away safety equipment when leaving the aircraft (lifejackets have been found in fishing boats!).
- damage all or part of the aircraft...

Western passengers are far from behaving perfectly. There have been cases of of hostesses and stewards being subject to aggression[8] but it is hard to imagine a western airline issuing such a warning on its website.

On the other hand, there was nothing up-market about the treatment meted out to Vladivostok Avia's passengers. At the time of the accident, the catering service was in the middle of a re-organisation programme. As a result a lot of passengers complained about the food served on board saying it was no better than that served in their garrison mess. In spite of an 8½ hour flight, they were only served a frugal meal consisting of a "snack with meat or fish accompanied by olives and vegetables."

Have a good flight!

---

[7] 515 Euros at the time of going to press.

[8] Read PASSAGERS INCONTROLABLES by the same author, published by Altipresse

At **19:47**, Flight XF 352 left Yekaterinburg airport. It took off from Runway 08 right[9]. A few moments later it checked the beacon "Kilo Uniform" and carried on climbing, heading east. Koltsovo control cleared it to change to the approach frequency, 125.9.

Before resuming this account, it is worth giving some background detail about the metric system used by the Russians aboard their aircraft. They have never brought themselves round to adopting the Anglo-Saxon measurement system that predominates in aviation. Russian pilots still speak in kilometres per hour for speed, metres for the altitude and millimetres of mercury for atmospheric pressure. Western pilots consider this to be bit crazy, but that is the way it is. There is nothing ideological behind all this. It is a matter of pure logic: the metric system is not adapted to aeronautics. Even the French have come round to admitting this. In their splendid old-fashioned manner, the Russians have never managed to get round to making the great reform that would bring them to work with the same aeronautical standards as the rest of the world. Maybe one day?

In the following re-transcription, it is possible that some expressions will surprise pilots who have never flown in Russia.

The Tupolev now levelled out at 10,050 metres![10]

It was still daytime[11], but as the aircraft was flying at 562 mph eastwards, night would fall very quickly for those who were aboard.

At around 21 hours, the meal was over and the hostesses quickly removed the trays. The passengers soon dozed off and the first three hours of the trip were perfectly peaceful.

At **01:35** in the morning, the Tupolev was 218 miles from Irkutsk; the controller gave it clearance to start its descent to level 5,700 m (18,700 ft). The Navigator was talking on the radio and he estimated they would be landing in thirty minutes or so.

---

[9] In reality, the words "right" and "left" used for the two runways at Yekaterinburg are not appropriate because although they have the same QFU 08/26 they are not parallel and diverge by more than ten degrees. Besides, the northern runway is totally unusable. It has been under repair for a long time now and even the taxiways separating the two runways cannot be used.

[10] 33,000 feet or level 330 for a western pilot.

[11] At Yekaterinburg on 4 July the sun sets at 22 hours 52 minutes local time.

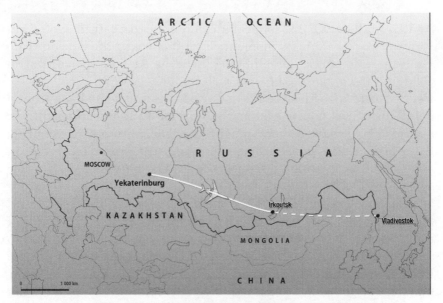

The journey from Yekaterinburg to Vladivostok.
The aircraft first flies over Russia to Irkutsk. Then, in the second part of the
trip it flies well into China for over 950 miles before flying back over Russian
territory a few miles, then landing at Vladivostok.
Yekaterinburg – Irkutsk: 1,750 miles
Irkutsk – Vladivostok: 1,437 miles

Irkutsk Airport is hardly a big international airline hub. Situated to the south-east of the city near the Angara dam, its installations date back to the Soviet era. As is often the case in Russia, the runway is rather rudimentary. Oriented 12/30, there are no ground markings: no centre line, no numbers painted on the cement to show distances, let alone threshold figures on the QFU indicating that the aircraft is lining up for the correct runway. In fact it is just a strip of cement the pilots have to cope with as best they can. Air traffic is relatively limited at Irkutsk with the only foreign airlines landing there being Chinese or Korean. The infrastructure for instrument landings is strictly minimal and there is no ILS system enabling the aircraft to make an accurate instrument approach[12]. Approaches are made either with the help of an old Non Directional Beacon "India Romeo" or with help from the "India Romeo Kilo" VOR[13]. In both cases, the minima are not

---

[12] Some unofficial documents suggest there is an ILS system at Irkutsk, but that it broke down long ago.

[13] India Romeo beacon frequency: 514 KHz. India Romeo Kilo beacon frequency: 112.3 MHz.

really operational when the weather is bad. This lack of equipment is surprising since Irkutsk is hardly the sunniest spot in the world. This is eastern Siberia! The weather there is often atrocious since the artificial lake on the Angara has created a particularly humid micro-climate. And then, there is the huge Lake Baikal, not even a hundred miles away, the biggest fresh water supply in the world, stretching over 375 miles north to south. Depending on wind direction, the air is loaded with humidity and Irkutsk airport is frequently fog-bound.

When this happens, airliners have no other choice but to divert to Bratsk airport, 312 miles to the north. The phenomenon is all the more surprising because the fog is extremely localised. When visibility is barely 100 metres at Irkutsk, 20 miles further east, the weather is often fine[14].

By chance, the weather that night was excellent. There were a few clouds here and there above the lake but generally visibility was good. Not the slightest trace of fog.

At **01:40**, the Navigator received the latest weather forecast from Irkutsk. The ATIS then gave him the "X-Ray" information: "the QFE is 710 mm of mercury; there's a westerly 290 degree wind, at 5 knots. There are no significant clouds over the airport"[15].

Runway 30 was in service and this was normal: when the wind was calm, it was the one controllers used to avoid aircraft overflying the town. This was two in the morning and the Tupolev was not exactly discreet. Even descending on idle throttle it was extremely noisy.

The crew were going to start their approach with the help of the radio-compass and would finish visually. But it would not be a classic racecourse-shaped pattern. Visibility was excellent. The aircraft would proceed to the left downwind for runway 30. It would fly over Lake Angara then make two left turns one after the other to place it on the final approach.

It would not be difficult that evening because the town lights were visible from far off. Besides, the Tupolev would be followed during

---

[14] There is another runway to the north of Irkutsk. However, it does not have any equipment for blind landings and is reserved for the Sukhoi aircraft factories that build fighter jets and the Beriev factories that build forest fire-fighting flying boats.

[15] Information given by the recorded ATIS tape. To avoid controllers having to repeat endlessly which runway is in service, what the weather conditions and the landing parameters are, each airport has an ATIS (Automatic Traffic Information Service) frequency. The message is usually renewed every hour and given an information letter. In the present case this was X (for X-Ray).

the approach by Irkutsk radar. This was not the most up-to-date system but at this late hour, there was only one aircraft in the sector and the controller was hardly overworked.

It was now **01:50**. What follows is the transcript of the recording taken from the Cockpit Voice Recorder[16]. The Tupolev 154 flew over the Yenisseï Basin; it had just passed abeam Tcheremchanka. The First Officer was at the controls but the aircraft was flying on Autopilot. Sitting behind him was the Navigator in contact with the Irkutsk approach on frequency 131.70 MHz.
The Captain was watching.

The controller had just given him clearance for descent but as the aircraft was a bit too high, the First Officer went about correcting this with considerable energy and, unwittingly or not, he adopted a nose down pitch attitude that made the aircraft hurtle along at top speed towards Irkutsk.
At **01:57**, the Tupolev dropped through the 6,500 m (21,125 ft) level, still at high speed. It crossed the "Razdolye" reporting point at 356 mph. Even at night, this point was easily recognisable because it is abeam of the small village of Ussolia-Sibirskaya. A little further on, to the left, there was also the village of Angarsk on the River Angara.

The Navigator called Irkutsk radar a minute later.

01:58:07 (Navigator): *845, we're reaching level 5,700 metres.*

It was late and the controller's voice showed signs of tiredness.

01:58:10 (Irkutsk radar): *Copied 845, I have radar contact. You've just gone past Razdolye at 5,700 m. Contact approach on 125.20.*

01:58:21 (Navigator): *125.20... Good night.*

Sitting in the left-hand seat, the Captain continued to observe matters. He did not speak into the radio. Unlike in a two-man "Western" crew, he simply gave instructions or continued to grant approval without ever intervening. For the time being, the First Officer was at the controls, and he left him to it.

---

[16] The original Russian was translated by Ariel Beresniak and Anna Larovaia and now translated from the French by Alan McKay.

01:58:21 (Captain): *Okay!*

As the frequency was already set, the Navigator merely had to flip the switch to be in contact with Irkutsk approach.

01:58:22 (Navigator): *Irkutsk approach, this is 85 845, evening. We're passing Razdolye at 5,700 metres and we've received information X-Ray.*

01:58:32 (Irkutsk approach): *85 845 Irkutsk approach, evening... you're on radial 282 degrees, distance 80 km. Report 2,700 m and keep on heading to downwind... It'll be a left-hand circuit.*

The controller's instructions were perfectly normal for an aircraft arriving at Irkutsk from the west and they also helped the crew gain time by avoiding a long and painstaking NDB procedure. The Tupolev was going to make its approach from south of the airport as with a visual day-time approach. The crew would just have to avoid flying over the dam, considered to be a strategic zone. Overflying it was forbidden, even for an airliner. The aircraft would therefore give it a wide berth to the south and proceed to the left downwind for Runway 30. Then, when it arrived abeam the India Romeo beacon[17], it would veer to the left twice as if it was doing a visual approach. At that point, it would be on final approach for runway 30. All the First Officer would have to do was let the aircraft go down on a suitable glide path and find the Irkutsk runway right in front of his windscreen. There was no particular difficulty attached to the task, all the more so in so far as just a mile and a half from the runway there was another beacon to tell the crew it was right on the axis.

This type of NDB approach is no longer used nowadays in major airports but the Tupolev crew were used to it. Even if there were some clouds to the south-east, this was no problem since their base was at about 1,000 m.
So tonight, it was just routine!
In a calm voice, the Navigator confirmed that he had understood the controller's instructions:

01:58:43 (Navigator): *Copied 845... joining downwind and we descend to 2,700 m.*

---

[17] The Morse signal for the beacon is "IR" and the frequency is 514.

All was perfectly calm in the cockpit. There was no perceptible strain and the only discordant note came from the First Officer who continued to push the aircraft at full speed towards the position he had been asked to reach. The airspeed indicator was nearing the never exceed red line but nobody complained. After all, the night was calm, the aircraft was solid and there was no turbulence. Everyone was in a hurry to land. Refuelling at Irkutsk would take 40 minutes and the sooner they were on the ground, the sooner they would be able to get away again. This was only the first half of the flight and the night would be a long one, so the First Officer's haste met with approval.

A few moments later the Captain took a look out of the windscreen to evaluate the weather towards his destination. What he saw suited him fine:

01:59:25 (Captain): *It seems very good!*

Ahead, at eleven o'clock, you could see the lights of the town, confirmation that there was no fog at Irkutsk that night and so no need to divert to Bratsk as so often happened. All was well.

01:59:35 (Captain): *It'll take us 550 metres from the downwind…*

The City of Irkutsk by night, with the main square perfectly visible on the banks of the River Angara.

The Captain had just made a strange comparison between the approach he generally made at Vladivostok and the one he was now performing. This was understood later. There is some ambiguity here, but it would appear that, according to his calculations, he thought the rate of descent set by the First Officer was too high. However, he did not have time to take his reasoning any further because as they got closer to the downwind leg, a thick layer of cloud loomed up in front of the aircraft. This was unsurprising since they were getting close to the lake but it was best to take precautions. The Captain pointed to the anti-icing system switch for the air intakes:

02:01:04 (Captain): *Looks as though we'll have to put them on.*

In fact, the Tupolev was going into and out of a succession of clouds at full speed. Although the lights were not on, it was an exhilarating sensation. Then, the Captain spoke once again to the Navigator. As was often the case aboard a Russian aircraft, he addressed him by his first name:

02:01:42 (Captain): *Yura, switch on the Pitot heating.*

02:01:43 (Flight Engineer): *OK, switched on!*

A few seconds later, the Irkutsk controller called:

02:01:55 (Irkutsk Radar controller): *845, you're at 40 kilometres. Descend to 2,100 metres and maintain.*

02:01:58 (First Officer): *Ok... 2,100 metres.*

The First Officer had just instinctively confirmed the height for which they were cleared but it was not up to him to answer. Everybody had their own job to do. The Navigator took up the microphone.

02:01:59 (Navigator): *Roger... 845, descending to 2,100.*

Then suddenly, the Captain returned to the comparison he had made a few moments earlier.

02:02:59 (Captain): *At home, when we make a straight in approach, we go past DAGES at this altitude... Here we've got to lose more than 550 metres...*[18]

The DAGES reporting point was "at home" for him, on the axis of Runway 07/25 at Vladivostok[19], i.e. more than 1,875 miles from Irkutsk. The situation seemed comparable to him because he always went past the point after losing 550 metres from downwind. One cannot help thinking that his reasoning was rather strange. It would have been more professional to have had in mind an approach chart for Irkutsk! Apparently, these remarks had no effect on the First Officer's behaviour. The aircraft continued its rapid descent and the airspeed indicator was still at 356 mph. The controller called back two minutes later to check that the crew had the right information for their landing. As we have already seen, these data were given on a recording that was brought up to date every hour. It was now 2 o'clock in the morning and the tape had just been updated. The "X-Ray" information had been changed to "Yankee" and, conscientiously, the controller wished to know whether the crew was aware of this.

02:04:09 (Irkutsk Radar Controller): *845... the latest weather is now "Yankee"... confirm you have received Yankee?*

02:04:13 (Navigator): *Roger, I'm listening to it right now.*

To show that he had indeed received the new information, he turned up the sound of the ATIS. Everybody in the cockpit could hear the recorded tape.

02:04:21 (Recorded tape of the ATIS): *710 millimetres... QFE 947, no significant changes... Confirm you have received information Yankee on first contact.*

However, the message was so loud that it drowned out the radio exchanges. The Captain spoke to Kolya:

---

[18] The Captain mistakenly used the word "altitude" here. He should have said "height". Altitude is measured in relation to the sea, height in relation to the ground at the airport. As the Tupolev pilots were working with the QFE, he was constantly working using the "height" concept.

[19] The airline's head office was at Vladivostok.

02:04:43 (Captain): *Kolya, you listen to the ATIS and I'll talk to the control, OK.*

02:04:45 (Kolya, the Navigator): *OK I'm listening.*

02:04:49 (Captain to controller): *845, we're arriving at 2,100 metres.*

02:04:52 (Approach controller): *Roger, 845, what type of approach are you going to make?*

02:04:55 (Captain): *We're going to make an NDB approach...*[20] *We have the Yankee information and er... the altimeter is at 710 millimetres*[21].

02:05:02 (Radar control): *Okay 845, you are cleared for an NDB approach. Descend to 900 metres for base leg, altimeter setting 710...*

02:05:08 (Captain): *845 Roger, descending to 900 metres for left base leg... Altimeter 710.*

From now onwards, the approach evolved into a sort of large circuit at the end of which the Tupolev would overfly the beacon situated on the runway axis. Nothing but the most basic stuff at Irkutsk. This was all the easier because the weather was good and the controller was keeping an eye on the Tupolev's flight path on the radar.

02:05:14 (Radar controller): *You are now downwind, distance: 11 kilometres.*

02:05:18 (Captain): *Yes copied... we have the field in sight.*

The Tupolev had just come out of the clouds... To the left, they could see the glowing lights of the town (position 1). To the south,

[20] By using the radio-compass beacon "India Romeo" mentioned above.
[21] The specialists noted that the Russian pilots still did their breakthrough using the QFE (atmospheric pressure on the ground at the airport) whereas the rest of the world uses the ONH (atmospheric pressure adjusted to sea level). Besides, this pressure is expressed in millimetres of mercury (710 in the present case) whereas it is expressed in hectopascals everywhere else. You can imagine all the conversions western pilots have to do when landing in Russia.

on the other hand, all was in darkness. Not the slightest light because there were still clouds over the Angara.

No matter... Just along the edge of the shore, a faint streak of light could be discerned - the Irkutsk runway. Nothing like the runway lights of a big airport, just low density lamps, some of which were even burnt out. But there was no mistaking it. This was well and truly the 12/30 appearing already to the north. They would be landing in about 8 minutes, right on schedule.

However, the First Officer showed no sign of seeking to decelerate. At 02:05:22 the airspeed indicator was still at 337 mph[22] and this was beginning to be problematic since this was much too fast to lower the landing gear. The Tupolev was an extremely robust aircraft, but even it had structural limits. If the landing gear was lowered at that speed the slipstream would cause considerable damage to the landing gear doors. They could even be ripped off.

The procedure required the speed to be less than 250 mph for lowering the landing gear. They had to slow down.

But for the moment nobody said anything.

The First Officer's only worry seemed to be switching off the anti-icing systems because the Tupolev was now flying in a completely clear sky and they were to no purpose.

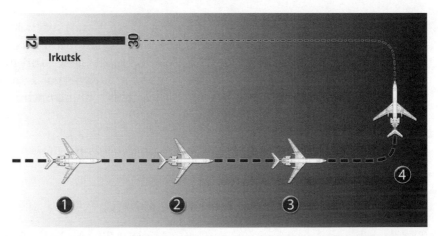

02:05:28 (First Officer talking to the Flight Engineer): *Yura, it's clear. We could switch them off. We'll see later.*

The Captain agreed immediately.

02:05:29 (Captain): *Yeah, okay, agreed.*

---

[22] 292 knots.

Remember this is a Russian aircraft where tasks were shared out among the crew. So the Navigator, Kolya, rather than the Captain or the First Officer plotted the route and the latter had to follow his instructions.

02:05:32 (Navigator): *I'm waiting for us to be 20 kilometres away...*

02:05:35 (Captain): *Okay.*

The Navigator was quite logically going to have the aircraft fly away on the downwind leg (position 2). The aircraft would then turn to the left so as to check the beacon.
Up until now, the flight path had been correct and all was well except that the aircraft was still hurtling along at 337 mph, much too fast for an airport circuit. But the crew knew it was 2 in the morning and they were alone in the flying zone with no risk of running into any other traffic. Things would have been different in crowded air space and the controller would have imposed a speed limit[23].

02:05:36 (Navigator): *We're setting the altimeters now... 710 millimetres on mine.*

02:05:43 (Captain): *Spoilers deployed... We have to slow down... Reduce speed!*

02:05:44 (unidentified voice): *Slow down, slow down.*

But the First Officer failed to react and the aircraft continued to race ahead. It was time to extend the landing gear but this was impossible at such a speed. A feeling of tense exasperation was now starting to build up in the cockpit.

02:05:47 (Captain): *We're setting the altimeters at 710 millimetres.*

02:05:48 (First Officer): *OK... 710.*

02:5:49 (unidentified voice): *710....*

---

[23] In the terminal zones of airports, the maximum speed allowed is 250 knots (281 mph) but if the traffic increases controllers can ask pilots to reduce their speed further. Depending on the aircraft this can be limited to 180 knots.

Having set all the altimeters to the same setting, the Captain called the controller to indicate his height.

02:05:55 (Captain calling controller): *845, we're going through 1,800 metres descending, altimeter 710. We'll call you reaching 1,250 metres descending to 900 metres.*

This message was absolutely superfluous since the aircraft was already cleared to descend to 900 metres. Besides, why waste time giving details that already appear on the controller's radar screen? The controller could only approve:

02:06:01 (Controller): *Roger.*

The aircraft continued flying at the same speed, going so fast that it only took a few seconds to reach the requested height. The Navigator warned the First Officer immediately:

02:06:03 (Navigator): *We're only 150 metres from requested height…*

02:06:04 (First Officer): *Yes…*

The First Officer approved but did not react, letting the aircraft hurtle round the circuit like a missile. The Captain now showed some irritation and his tone became more incisive:

02:06:05 (Captain): *Slow down… reduce your speed!*

02:06:05 (First Officer): *I am reducing it… I am reducing it…*

His voice was slightly strained; clearly he was in a "phase lag". He was not anticipating what was going to happen. It was as if the aircraft was deciding for him. It was a classical failing that all instructors recognise readily in their students whereby they seek to correct a situation once a mistake has been made but when it is obviously too late.
The Navigator also realised that the First Officer was being passive. He too let fly a warning at him:

02:06:06 (Navigator): *Watch out, mechanisation!*

This meant lowering the flaps. But as with the landing gear, lowering them at high speed could cause structural damage. The Tupolev was obviously still going too fast. The reason for this excessive speed was simple. The First Officer had reduced the thrust but the aircraft was still on a steep descent path so it could not slow down.

02:06:08 (Captain): *We're coming to 100 metres of assigned (height)...*

02:06:09 (First Officer): *That's affirmative... We're at 100 metres.*

His voice was increasingly strained. It was clear that the First Officer was tense. He would have liked to master his machine but could not do so. An aircraft cannot be slowed down like a car but moves in an unstable environment where you just cannot apply the brakes - especially during a descent!

02:06:10 (Navigator): *... kilometres...*

The Navigator was probably announcing that the aircraft was now 12½ miles from the runway. They would soon have to turn to the left (position 3). Meanwhile, despite his efforts, the First Officer had still failed to bring things under control as the speed was still some 312 mph.
And that point, the Captain started to lose his temper.

02:06:13 (Captain): *You've set an 8 metres per second descent rate...[24] That's why you're going so fast!*

At that very moment, the aircraft entered the clouds again. It was now close to Lake Baikal; the level of humidity was much higher and the temperature much cooler. They could no longer see the ground lights and they were in pitch black darkness again.

02:06:17 (Captain): *Let's go, Yura... Now we're in the clouds.*

Despite the circumstances, the Captain asked to check the weather forecast at Irkutsk airport. You could never be too cautious... Although it was July, it was still the middle of a Siberian night

---

[24] About 1,600 feet for a western pilot.

and the ground temperature could drop rapidly. If it got close to the dew point, there would be a risk of fog.

02:06:20 (Captain): *Look... what temperature is it over there?*

02:06:21 (Navigator re-reading aloud the information he received from the ATIS): *So... they gave us wind from 290 degrees 5 knots... temperature 14 degrees... 710 millimetres... and Cavok[25].*

Why worry? There was no doubt about weather conditions at Irkutsk being excellent. Once the Tupolev came out of this small layer of clouds the crew would be able to see the runway again and they would be able to land without the slightest difficulty. It was a simple breakthrough! All the more so in so far as the First Officer had realised his mistake and had actually decided to decelerate. To do so, he had reduced his descent rate and the thrust on all three engines completely.

Note that while going through this layer of clouds, the crew no longer had any outside visual landmarks. The aircraft's attitude had to be monitored using the instruments. This was the basis of flying in Instrumental Meteorological Conditions. Nothing complicated... a properly trained pilot should know how to fly his aircraft with an Attitude Director indicator.

02:06:25 (Captain): *Alright.*

The engines were now running on idle and the airspeed continued to drop little by little. It was now 293 mph...

It was still too high to lower the landing gear but they were getting closer to the right configuration. The Flight Engineer carried out a few adjustments. With the aircraft still in the clouds, he checked in particular that the Autopilot was still connected. Note that, up until now the crew had not carried out any checklists, this not being the recommended procedure for this type of aircraft. Rather, they all kept an eye on each other and checked that nothing had been forgotten.

02:06:32 (Captain): *How many kilometres remaining before we turn?*

---

[25] Ceiling And Visibility OK.

02:06:34 (Navigator): *Another 8 kilometres.*

02:06:34 (First Officer): *Roger 8 kilometres ...*

02:06:35 (Captain): *Copied....*

21 seconds later, the Tupolev reached a height of 900 metres. Unfortunately the airspeed was still 275 mph, much too high to contemplate extending the landing gear.

02:06:56 (Captain): *OK, take it like that. I've switched hold altitude.*

From this moment onwards, the Autopilot was connected to stabilise the aircraft. Whatever speed was set for the engines, the system would try to maintain 900 metres.

02:06:58 (First Officer): *Okay.*

02:07:02 (First Officer): *400 kilometres per hour.*

In fact, the First Officer was cheating with the figures. The aircraft was still at 262 mph but time was running out, and of course the difference did not seem that significant. It is highly unlikely that the 12 extra mph would have caused irreparable damage to the airframe... but aviation is a world of precision where vague approximations have no place. The Captain however remained unperturbed and immediately announced:

02:07:03 (Captain): *It's OK for the rudder... Gear down.*

02:07:06 (First Officer): *Putting down...*

The First Officer placed his hand on the lever and lowered it. Unlike most aircraft, the Tupolev's nose wheel is not underneath the flight deck (see photo) and the crew could hear nothing of the mechanisms whirling away beneath the fuselage floor. Only the indicators on the instrument panel showed that the process was under way.
The Flight Engineer confirmed immediately:

02:07:08 (Flight Engineer): *Gear is going down.*

At that moment, engine power was on full idle. There was not the slightest sensation of thrust and the aircraft resembled nothing so much as a huge 100-ton glider. The drag suddenly caused by lowering the landing gear had the effect of a huge speed brake and the airspeed dropped abruptly to 243 mph. Whereas twenty seconds earlier the Tupolev was going too fast, now it was going a little too slow. Another instance of the phase lag phenomenon with one big mistake leading to excessive corrective action that itself induces a new, opposite, compounded mistake...

The First Officer was ready to announce that the landing gear was down:

02:7:10 (First Officer): *The landing gear is....*

But the controller's voice resounded in the speakers before he had finished speaking.

02:07:12 (Radar controller): *845, turn to base leg. Descend 850 metres for final.*

02:07:17 (Captain speaking to the radio): *Roger 845... Down to 850 metres for final.*

02:07:21 (Flight Engineer): *Gear down and locked!*

The situation was suddenly becoming dangerous due to the extremely low speed.
This brutal braking had three causes:
    - The engines were idling and the First Officer had failed to re-adjust power: there was no more thrust.
    - Levelling out at 900 metres, the aircraft had stopped descending, which compounded the braking effect.
    - The huge landing gear was now down. The engineers had designed it so the aircraft could land on beaten earth and its size made for an enormous drag effect. To get an idea of its dimensions all you have to do is compare it with the main Airbus A 321 landing gear, which only has four wheels. The Tupolev had 12 and they were big low pressure tires[26].
Now, an aircraft needs airspeed to fly with the speed generating lift. No speed and you stall. The Captain immediately warned:

---

[26] An Airbus 321 and a Tupolev 154 carry roughly the same number of passengers.

02:07:23 (Captain): *OK... But the speed is decreasing too much...*

And as the aircraft was at 900 metres and they had been asked to go down to 850 metres, the Captain pursued with a slightly authoritarian tone of voice:

02:07:25 (Captain): *Descend!*

In response, the First Officer just turned the Autopilot control but did nothing to adjust power. So the airspeed dropped further to 237 mph. As a result, the lift dropped too and the consequences were felt immediately as the aircraft began to sink by itself.
The Captain naturally understood that he had to increase the thrust but his reaction was far from swift.

02:07:27 (Captain): *Keep 850 metres and you set 70% of NI for the thrust.*

In front of his console, the Flight Engineer pushed the levers forward and confirmed the Captain's order.

02:07:29 (Engineer): *Agreed... 70...*

Unfortunately this was not enough and the speed continued to drop. It was now only 225 mph and in that configuration the minimum airspeed recommended by the manufacturer was 230 mph. As a result, the aircraft became slightly unstable. It was almost imperceptible but it just did not have that extra 6 mph that would have made it that bit healthier. This was all the more important since the First Officer had just gone off into a left turn as the controller had asked him to. The bank angle reached 23 degrees (position 4).

The Captain was starting to get worried. The aircraft was becoming more unstable. This was nothing serious in itself, just a bit of trembling that could be passed off as due to slight turbulence. But this could be the sign that the beast slumbering inside the machine could well and truly awaken.
The Captain ordered a further increase in power.

02:07:30 (Captain): *350 kph (218 mph)... speed in range... set 75% N1.*

02:07:33 (Engineer): *Roger 7 – 5.*

02:07:37 (Navigator): *Approaching 850 metres.*

The situation was deteriorating but not yet dramatic. All that was
needed was to push the throttle fully forward for a few seconds
and, above all, not pull back on the stick.
The Captain came in again:

02:07:39 (Captain): *Power 80.*

02:07:40 (Engineer): *80.*

Still not enough... What was happening was fairly conventional.
Little by little, as the aircraft's nose goes up, the drag increases,
the airspeed remains bridled and the angle of attack increases.
In this instance, it was almost as if the crew were seeking to stall
the aircraft. The speed went down imperceptibly to 216 mph, then
back up to 218 mph.
The Captain intervened again but once more his reaction was lame:

02:07:42 (Captain): *82%.*

02:07:43 (Engineer): *OK 82.*

02:07:44 (Navigator): *We're at 850 metres.*

02:07:45 (Captain): *Roger 850 metres.*

Speed was maintained with some difficulty at 218 mph. The
aircraft was still turning. The angle of attack was still high and
the crew were still not really taking any effective measures. They
should have set to full throttle without hesitating but instead the
Captain merely reacted in short bursts. This was not enough and
the Autopilot reacted in its own manner in seeking to maintain
height at 850 metres, pulling up too. It was a kind of vicious circle.
The more the Tupolev slowed down, the more the nose rose up on
the horizon and the angle of attack reached 16.5 degrees.
The First Officer seemed unaware of all this.

02:07:47: this time marked the beginning of the tragedy.

The increase in the angle of attack set off a strident alarm. At that moment, there was nothing else to do but push softly on the stick and open up the three engine throttles.

But the First Officer took the wrong option. Surprised by the sudden alarm, he pushed the stick forward violently. The movement was so brutal that it deactivated the Autopilot. A second alarm sounded to warn them that the AP had been disconnected and that the aircraft would now have to be flown manually.

The Captain realised that things were definitely taking a turn for the worse and responded angrily:

02:07:49 (Captain): *Fuck, what the hell are you doing?*

02:07:51 (Captain): *Speed!!*

Unfortunately he did not take over the controls...

Further panicked by being chastised this way, the First Officer pushed the stick again but his actions were ever clumsier. By pushing, he banked the aircraft even further to the left, first by 30 degrees, then 44 degrees and 48 degrees... The speed went back up to 250 mph but as the aircraft was still in the clouds the First Officer did not realise this and kept banking.

The Captain exploded:

02:07:53 (Captain): *Fuck, push up the throttle!!!*

One might well wonder why the Captain just gave out orders rather than simply taking over the controls. Perhaps strain or stress prevented him from reacting. Maybe events were unfolding too quickly. Nobody will ever know. In all events, he failed to respond rapidly. In addition, the Russian arrangement that involved a large number of crew members on the flight deck here caused a problem in that it reduced their individual sense of responsibility. All of them had more or less access to the controls but, in that emergency situation, each of them relied on the others to make the right move. Clearly, the "Crew Resource Management" techniques[27] taught around the world were quite unknown to Vladivostok Avia.

And in such circumstances, there can be a complete lack of initiative. Here, all that could be heard were incomprehensible

---

[27] A management technique enabling crew resources to be applied to ensure maximum efficiency and safety.

orders blurted out wildly in the cockpit and the crew member with the least experience among the four (the First Officer) and who had no idea what to do was the one at the controls!

02:07:53 (First Officer): *Stop... Stop... Where? Where?*

These ramblings show how truly lost he was. Everything was moving too fast and, disturbed as he was, the First Officer had lost spatial awareness. The aircraft was still in the clouds, there were no outside markers and no horizon could be seen in the night - not the slightest light that could enable them to better perceive the aircraft's position. There was only the artificial horizon on the instrument panel to indicate that the Tupolev was banking steeply, but the First Officer was not even looking at it.

The human brain is not made for flying blind. The best pilot in the world would be unable to keep the wings horizontal without assistance from instruments. An instrument panel is needed together with knowledge on how to use it. An American study showed that a beginner can fly without instruments for exactly... 178 seconds. A little less than three minutes. After that time, they lose all sense of spatial awareness, suffer from vertigo and no longer know where vertical is. They can fly an aircraft upside down without realising it, thinking they are the right way up.

In the case of the Tupolev, it took much less time for the whole crew to become spatially disorientated. After a dozen or so seconds, the First Officer no longer knew how he was flying. His reactions then became tragically typical as he pushed the stick randomly to the right and the left. Panic overwhelmed the cockpit.

02:07:55 (Captain): *Stop... Stop... Stop.*

02:07:55 (Navigator): *This way... This way... This way...*

The Captain finally decided to take control of the aircraft in the middle of all this cacophony.

Unfortunately his intervention was scarcely more effective than his First Officer's, worse even. First, he corrected to the left, i.e. the exact opposite of what he ought to have done. Then, he corrected to the right. Then, again to the left, but even more so. His movements were brutal and confused, just like a trainee who has just discovered a flight simulator for the first time. His actions on the stick went from right to left for no real reason often moving in the opposite direction to the artificial horizon.

The bank angle was between 30 and 45 degrees to the left. Everybody was panicking!

02:07:57 (Captain): *We're recovering!*

Unfortunately autosuggestion does not provide the best technique for flying an aircraft. It is not enough to say you are safe for the situation to stabilise by itself. For two long seconds, the aircraft continued to roll from right to left while retaining a slight dive, but it did not return to level flight.

In the cabin, the passengers had been woken by the jolts and the first screams could be heard.

At this stage recovery remained a possibility. A well-trained pilot could easily have brought the machine back under control. He would have had to concentrate on the instrument panel, perform calm and precise movements while looking at the artificial horizon only. First, as a priority, bring the wings back to the horizontal, then stabilise the aircraft level. The problem was that the two pilots at the controls were used to connecting an Autopilot and had lost the habit of basic flying. They were completely overwhelmed by the situation.

Strangely enough, the only one who seemed to realise that the last thing to do was to handle the controls brutally was the Navigator.

02:07:58 (Navigator): *Easy... take it easy.*

02:07:59 (First Officer): *Let's move it to the right...*

Here the First Officer was correct! The aircraft was still banking by more than 45 degrees to the left. To get the wings horizontal again, the stick would have to be applied to the right and above all not insist on the wrong side as the Captain had been doing for the last few seconds.

The radio altimeter alarm went off at the same time. It sounded for four seconds to warn that the aircraft was getting dangerously close to the ground. This was accompanied by the AOA alarm: the angle of attack was too high![28]

---

[28] Angle of Attack: when this goes beyond a critical value, the aircraft stalls whatever the speed it is flying at.

02:08:02 (strained unidentified voice): *Power... Add thrust!*

This time, total panic broke out... Everyone understood that things were deteriorating rapidly. The aircraft's rate of fall had just increased to 20 metres per second[29]. It was at this moment that someone made a terrible mistake. The Tupolev's flight data recorder was not sophisticated enough to reveal who between the Captain and the First Officer was responsible for this irreparable blunder. Seeing the rate of fall increase, one of them pulled abruptly on the stick, a disastrous reflex in the circumstances. With the aircraft engaged in a steep turn, the angle of attack increased drastically and the Tupolev immediately stalled.

02:08:05 (strained, very high pitched, unidentified voice): *Power!*

02:08:06 (Flight Engineer): *Got it!*

From his seat, the Flight Engineer pushed the throttles full forward. The N1 regime started to set off again slowly... But a jet is not a piston engine. You have to wait several long seconds before thrust returns. Worse... The Tupolev slipped onto the left wing and entered a spin, not an ordinary spin but a flat spin, the worst possible situation for an airliner. Mastering such a situation involves an aerobatic manoeuvre reserved for a few very experienced pilots and is only done on competition single seaters, never with a transport aircraft. Even on such specially designed aircraft, it is difficult to get out of a flat spin as it tends to "feed" itself and the aircraft turns round on itself like a dead leaf. Generally, it rotates with the nose almost on a level with the horizon. It is a terrifying figure because the aircraft descends flat and the pilot has little choice as to how to get out of it...[30]

What made matters worse was the fact that the Tupolev 154 had an aerodynamic profile that tended to exacerbate the flat spin due to its "T"-shaped tail (see photo) that causes the airstream on the elevators to be perturbed by the turbulence from the main wing. The controls become ineffective and auto-rotation becomes unstoppable.

---

[29] About 4,000 feet per minute.

[30] To get a better idea of the subject, read "TECHNIQUE DU VOL ACROBATIQUE" by the same author published by Altipresse (a book for aerobatics professionals)

And the fall was hellish[31].

When the Tupolev started its spin, it was at about 660 metres above the ground. At that height, even an aerobatics aircraft would have had trouble getting out of it. How could a 100 ton airliner ever have any hope of succeeding?

In the cockpit, the crew saw the artificial horizon wobbling crazily. Somebody screamed:

02:08:08 (Unidentified voice): *Add thrust!*

02:08:09 (First Officer): *Take-off power set! Oh my God!*

In the middle of all this confusion, the First Officer was the one giving instructions. The Captain's silence probably betrayed the fact that he had understood that there was nothing that could be done.

The Flight Engineer's response was devastatingly blunt.

02:08:10 (Unidentified voice): *That's all guys, it's all over, fuck!!*

There were still a few shouts shortly followed by silence. Panic gave way to resignation. Unfortunately the agony was to last as one of the characteristics of a flat spin is that the rotation makes for a slow descent rate. The aircraft is spinning flat so fast that the wings are rather like helicopter blades as they create lift to delay the descent. The Tupolev thus turned round on itself for a full 21 long seconds. An eternity when you know that the only issue is death.

At first, the crew could not see what was going on outside. Only the artificial horizon wobbling madly told them that the end was inevitable.

Then, the aircraft came out of the clouds.

The lights on the ground whirled past the cockpit windscreen, appearing and then disappearing in a flash. Nobody spoke. Hands grasped the seats. Everyone had understood. All you could hear was the audio tone of the radio altimeter and the AOA howling continually.

---

[31] To get an idea of what happens when a Tupolev 154 M goes into a spin, see the video of the Caspian Airlines crash on 15 July 2009 at: http://www.youtube.com/watch?v=BXompjxYpl0 Note, On this video the Tupolev is in a normal spin not a flat spin.

In the cabin the passengers were wailing with fear.

02:08:32 the recording went dead. The Tupolev had just hit the ground near the village of Burkadovka, 35 kilometres from Irkutsk on the base leg. As is always the case in the flat spin type of impact, the aircraft fell on its belly in a perfectly vertical trajectory.

The explosion tore the darkness. There were no survivors. This was the 55th Tupolev 154 not to bring its passengers home safely. The final toll was 145 victims, with the presence of five extra passengers not listed on the manifest being confirmed.

Both black boxes were rapidly recovered. However, as is often the case in aircraft accidents, the first explanations put forward were fanciful. Thus a few hours afterwards, the Russian Minister Sergei Shoigu gave a press conference to explain as seriously as possible that "the three engines had all failed at the same time. It could be a problem with the fuel supply circuits."

The following day, in front of other journalists, Vladimir Razbezhkin, one of the airline's managers, announced that there had been an explosion and that this could have been the result of a kerosene leak but it could also be an attack. As nobody wanted to talk of terrorism, the idea of a crash caused by bad weather at Irkutsk was put forward. The aircraft had made two landing attempts before hitting the ground during the third attempt. It is difficult to understand which parameters led the specialists to engage in such speculation. All the more so in so far as the Russian authorities were extremely unwilling to see such rumours spread. To shed light on the crash the President, Vladimir Putin, asked his Prime Minister Mikhail Kasyanov to set up a proper commission of enquiry. This would publish its findings under Ilya Klabanov as quickly as possible. It is from the preliminary findings of this report that the present narrative has been drawn.

Questions have been raised as to whether such a tragedy could happen with a western aircraft. Although no tests have been carried out in real, live conditions, wind tunnel tests show that most airliners cannot go into a flat spin. Those equipped with fly-by-wire controls like Airbuses or the Boeing 777 could never run into such a situation since the computers monitor everything going on aboard the aircraft and intervene to correct human errors in the majority of cases. Furthermore, huge progress has been made in aerodynamics. In the event of a stall, the aircraft will descend flat without banking onto one wing and simply pushing the stick forward will allow lift to be regenerated.

However, people remain fallible and can make mistakes that even the best computers cannot always correct. An instance of this will be seen later in the present book.

After this accident, Vladivostok Avia decided to stop operating the old Tupolev 154s. Today it only has three left and they have been grounded, stored away in case they are needed. Let us all hope they will soon occupy a prominent place in a museum.

Nowadays the airline flies Tupolev 204s, which are much less problematic. These are the aircraft operated on the Yekaterinburg-Vladivostok route. They are still not equipped with the most up-to-date technology but they have a sufficiently long range to do the trip non-stop. The night stopover at Irkutsk has therefore been cancelled and the flight now only takes 7 hours and 20 minutes. Since the accident, the airline's image has changed considerably. In 2004, it became a member of IATA, which imposes safety standards the airline did not previously observe. Management had to get used to the idea that they would have to modernise their airline and they have purchased some Airbus A320s and A330s. Thanks to these aircraft, Vladivostok Avia now flies regularly to Europe, Canada and the USA.

Excellent but very tired

6 August 1997
Guam

Located off the Philippines, right in the middle of the Pacific Ocean, the island of Guam has special status. It is attached to the United States but is not part of its territory[1]. Despite its reduced size (just 28 by 6¼ miles), Washington attaches great strategic importance to this territory as it provides an advanced military position in the Marianas[2]. It is so important for the Pentagon that over the years, the American Army has acquired more than a third of the island's surface. There is a naval base, an air base, a coastguard base, radar stations and hundreds of hangars and military buildings of all sorts.

The army's presence however has not detracted from the island's tourist potential. This is the South Pacific, the climate is tropical, the water is turquoise and the beaches are from paradise. All these elements combined with a top level hotel infrastructure make it a privileged destination for Japanese and Korean tourists, especially with newly-weds who come to Guam for their honeymoon. The spot is a must for young Asian lovebirds and tour operators have clearly grasped what they can make out of this Venice of the Pacific. They propose all-inclusive trips at extremely competitive prices and whole charters of "Just marrieds" disembark every day at Wom Guam International Airport. Demand has been so strong that on certain Friday evenings, more than one hundred Jumbo jets land and unload tourists.

---

[1] Guam is not a state of the USA. The official designation of the island is "Unincorporated Territory of the United States". The residents of Guam have a very special status because although they are American citizens they do not have the right to vote.

[2] The Pentagon seems to want more because there is a project to build a naval base for nuclear-powered aircraft-carriers on Guam. If the project comes to fruition, the army will then own 40% of the island.

The aircraft in this story (Registration HL 7468).
The price of this Jumbo Jet was estimated at 42 million Euros by the
investigators.

It was against this background that in the summer of 1997, a Korean Air Boeing 747-300 flew the Seoul-Guam route. This was a scheduled flight due to arrive at 01:40. Normally, the night trip was made by an Airbus 300 but that airplane was replaced at the last minute by a Jumbo Jet as the Airbus did not have enough seats for the return flight to Seoul[3]. This sudden rush of extra passengers was partly due to the fact that the Korean airline sponsored the Guam athletics team. The return flight was to transport the athletes and all their accompanying staff who were going to take part in the South Pacific Games in the Samoan Islands.

The outward flight number was KE 801 and it was to be an easy haul of just 2,000 miles between Seoul and Guam. The aircraft was not full and this was just a hop for the long-haul aircraft which took just 4 hours and 10 minutes to cover the distance.

The Boeing 747 was a 300 series version, weighing 250 tons on take-off and far from being the most modern aircraft at the time of the events. It was still equipped with analogue instruments and its crew was required to do a great deal of work and calculations. Unlike the latest 400 series, which can be flown by a crew of two, the 747-300 needed three in the cockpit:
- A Captain.
- A First Officer.
- A Flight Engineer.

---

[3] The 747 can carry 385 passengers whereas the Airbus 300 only 250.

The Captain

Park Yung Chul was the Captain that night. He was 42 and a former military pilot who had logged 8,900 flying hours. He had an excellent file record and was even considered the best in the airline. Two months earlier, Park had been awarded the highest distinction granted to any Korean airline pilot: the Flight Safety Award. He had been decorated for having perfectly handled an engine failure on his 747. This problem had occurred at low altitude and he had managed to land while still scrupulously respecting the procedures. A ceremony had been organized and the medal awarded him by the President of the airline in person.

All the rest of Park Yung Chul's file is in keeping with this:

- In June 1997, two months before these events, he underwent a "proficiency check" on simulators: the instructor's comment was "excellent".

- A month earlier he had undergone an in-flight check following which he had been evaluated as "very much above the average level".

- His level of English was also qualified as "quite excellent" by the airline examiners.

So it was no run-of-the mill pilot at the controls of Flight 801. What is more, he was well familiar with the Island of Guam, having landed there many times, both by night and day. He had come in on a Boeing 727 when he was a young pilot and returned a number of times flying Jumbo jets. Also, before taking off that very evening, an instructor had shown him a video about the problems encountered on landing on the island. It was a procedure the airline imposed when a crew was landing at an airport that presented certain problems. The approach to Guam is rather special as the island is mountainous and the VOR beacon situated on the runway axis is on top of a hill, Mount Nimitz. The approach requires special monitoring so as to scrupulously respect the altitudes marked on the aeronautical maps. Some pilots have even nicknamed the Guam airfield as the "Black Hole".

Captain Park Yung Chul was well aware of all these problems. After the accident, his wife explained to investigators that on the morning of the flight, after sleeping between 11.00 and 13.30, the Captain left quickly for the airport "in order to prepare his flight with utmost care." She also told how Park Yung Chul was far from being in good shape as he had found the previous days tiring.

Three days earlier, he had done a rotation to Hong Kong that had turned out to be extremely difficult. He should have returned to Seoul on 3 August but unfortunately a cyclone had delayed his flight and he had had to just sit it out at the airport, piling on the stress and exhaustion... the flight had finally left 24 hours late. The airline schedulers realised that there would be a rest time regulation problem when Park landed at Seoul and the pilot would not be able to take off again for Dubai as planned since he had not had the legally required rest time. So he was given a night return trip to Guam. This was only 4 hours instead of 9 and above all, he would leave later. This would enable international regulations concerning compulsory rest times for aircrews to be respected.

Park Yung Chul therefore went home to sleep for a couple of hours, then returned to the airport. But this rest was far too short and the Captain was still very tired. After several nights at the controls of his aircraft, he had been subjected to jet lag which had profoundly disturbed his sleep cycles. We shall see later that several times during the Guam flight, he brought up the subject of the overwork he had been subjected to.

And as if all that was not enough, Park had been suffering from severe bronchitis for several days. A doctor had prescribed an antibiotic, analgesics and anti-inflammatory medication but Park had not taken anything. He knew perfectly well that these medicines induced drowsiness and that taking them was not advisable when driving a car let alone flying an aircraft. Without treatment his bronchitis did not get any better and he often coughed during the flight. Park Yung Chul was therefore an excellent pilot but that night, he was not in possession of all his faculties.

The First Officer

The First Officer was Song Kyung Ho, also 42 years of age and a former military pilot who had logged 4,000 flying hours. The man was just back from a private stay in the States and this was his first flight since his return.

He had seen the video showing the problems at Guam airport too but unlike his boss, he had only been to Guam once in his career as an aircrew member and that was a number of years ago.

Song Kyung Ho's professional file was perfectly good but far from being as excellent as Captain Park Yung Chul's. There were especially certain weaknesses in the way he carried out his

"non precision" approaches like that for Guam. During a test, one instructor had written the following comments: "a bit slow executing instructions and procedures." Another added that the way the First Officer performed this type of approach was "somewhat below what one might hope for".
The First Officer was nonetheless recognised as having "a standard level".

Song Kyung Ho had obviously heard of Captain Park who was a real celebrity in Korean Air and like many other pilots he admired him. This was the first time he was to fly under him.

The Flight Engineer

The Flight Engineer was Naal Suk-Hoon and, at 57, he was the oldest of the three. He had also chalked up the most flying hours: more than 13,000. He too was a well above average crewman. His professional file even put him among the best Flight Engineers in the airline. The examiners' comments were especially enthusiastic: "excellent", "very much above average", "no criticisms", and "brilliant".
Naal Suk-Hoon was returning from a rotation to the States. He had been to Anchorage and San Francisco following which he had had a day and a half's rest in Seoul. This was his first visit to Guam.

The Flight Attendants

The crew comprised 14 hostesses and stewards. Except for the principal Cabin Senior Director who was 37 and another hostess who was 42, all the others were very young, aged between 20 and 24.

The passengers

There were 237 passengers on board, mainly Koreans[4]. There were 6 very young children but as usual most of the clientele was made up of young newly-weds on their honeymoon. There was also an

---

[4] There were also 13 Americans and one New-Zealander.

important Korean politician, Shin Li-ha, the charismatic leader of the National Congress for New Politics Party. The man was travelling with his wife and a delegation of twenty leading members of his party. It was Thursday night and working meetings had been organized during the weekend in order to study the party's strategy for the forthcoming elections.

Before continuing with this account, it is important to explain the discipline reigning aboard Korean Air aircraft. Each airline has its own management method. Some are relaxed. These are generally small airlines employing limited numbers of crews, where the atmosphere is calm and procedures are carried out in a friendly spirit; everybody knows each other, fly regularly together and become friends, even meeting outside work. Then, there are the bigger airlines where fostering good relations among aircrews is not a real priority and where the organization is almost military. Discipline is rigorous and respect for the hierarchy leaves no room for laughter and jokes. No liberties are tolerated by the representative of authority and the slightest slackness is immediately punished. This rigid attitude is often encountered in certain Asian companies.
Korean Air was one of them.
The Captain is so powerful that he can break a subordinate's career with a simple remark. All that is required is a report signed by him for the culprit to be demoted, transferred or even sacked on the spot. Even a First Officer can be grounded permanently if his Captain so decides.

We shall see that this omnipotence can put the subordinates in such a position of inferiority that no-one dares tell the boss if he makes a mistake.

Flight 801 took off from Seoul-Gimpo at 21:53[5]. The aircraft climbed to its cruising altitude of 41,000 feet and it was authorised to set a direct heading to its destination. For this flight Captain Park Yung Chul decided he was going to fly the aircraft. The First Officer would deal with radiocommunications with the controllers.

The trip from Seoul was not a comfortable one for at that time of year the weather was unstable in the South Pacific; there were very deep zones of depression which created violent turbulence.

---

[5] For greater clarity, all times have been expressed in Guam local time.

The Boeing had been shaken about for almost two hours. Nothing to endanger the aircraft but the Captain had nevertheless left the "fasten seat belts" on all the time. The turbulence came to an end 50 minutes before arrival.

The weather was not the cause of the catastrophe that ensued but it was an "aggravating factor". The climate in the Guam region is pretty uniform throughout the year. In general it is fine in the morning. The sky becomes overcast during the afternoon and it rains until late into the night. The statistics give an average of 24 days of rain per month. This meteorological feature is more pronounced in July and August. Although the temperature is close to 27 degrees C, showers are all the more violent, particularly at night. They even develop into tropical-like downpours.

This was August and it was precisely this type of weather that prevailed over the region that night.

It was now 1 o'clock in the morning and it was raining all over the Marianas. The latest weather readings carried out at Agana airport announced visibility at 5¼ miles. The wind was faint. The cloud base was between 1,500 and 4,000 ft, but in places, storms were causing violent showers. This was not in itself a problem for the crew. The Boeing 747 was equipped with a very effective weather radar system that enabled it to avoid the big rain masses. Moreover, the ground controllers had an FPS-93 radar connected to a "long range" ASR-8. These two systems can also identify hazardous weather phenomena for aircraft.

That night, it was Runway 06 Left that was being used at Guam, but there was a problem with the technical systems at the airport: the "glide" of the ILS was out of order[6]. It was not in fact faulty but being maintained: technicians were now working on the system which would again be operational by dawn.

---

[6] The Instrument Landing System is a precision landing system that enables the pilot to position the aircraft on the ideal flight path to reach the runway. It gives two types of information:

   - The approach axis thanks to the "localiser".

   - The descent approach plan thanks to the "Glide". This was the system that was not working that night. As a result the Boeing could position itself on the runway axis but did not have a descent plan. The pilot therefore had to carry out his final approach by calculating his distance in relation to the runway. This is routine work for a qualified pilot.

Captain Park Yung was obviously aware of this problem because a Notam[7] had been issued and the information was available in any airport. Besides, after the first radio contact, the controller had warned the crew that the "Glide" was out of use.

The unavailability of this system did not preclude landing at Guam. There were other procedures enabling aircraft to land in perfect safety. Moreover, at the same time as the Boeing was getting ready to start its descent, another 747 was landing on Runway 06 Left. This was Continental Flight 760. The pilot applied the VOR/DME procedure that enabled the aircraft to land without glide. Despite the showers in the airport region, everything went normally. Once the aircraft was on the ground the controller asked the pilot to give him an idea of the weather conditions he had encountered as he was landing. He answered that he had had no problems: "visibility was excellent."

At **01:10**, Flight KE 801 was 281 miles from its destination. For the crew it was time to begin the descent. The CERAP controller[8] cleared them to leave level 410 to descend at discretion to an altitude of 2,600 ft[9]. As the aircraft was over the ocean, there was no relief to hinder them. Besides, there were only ten or so aircraft in the Guam zone and none of these was on the 747's route. This explains why the controller did not impose any altitude restriction. They could descend as they wished.

However, to begin with, Captain Park decided to remain at 41,000 feet. He preferred to start by holding a briefing for the benefit of his subordinates. This procedure was compulsory. The aim was to give the crew all the data needed to make the approach and landing.

Here is Park Yung Chul's briefing, ostensibly conducted according to the rule book:

01:11:51 (Captain): *I'll give you a short briefing... ILS is 110.30.. NIMITZ VOR is 115.30, the course 063 since visibility is 6, when we are in the visual approach, as I said before, set the VOR on number 2 and maintain the VOR. For the TOD, I will add 3 miles*

---

[7] Note to Airmen: information available for all the pilots (airports, work, over-flight prohibition, etc.). Regulations stipulate that before each take-off, crew members have to consult the Notams concerning their flight and destination.

[8] Centre Radar Approach.

[9] About 800 metres. Unlike in the previous chapter (Tupolev in a flat spin), these events took place in air space run by an American control. The altimetric references are not made in relation to the airport ground level (QFE) but in relation to sea level (QNH), which is why the figure 2,600 feet is not a height but an altitude.

from the VOR, and start descent when we're about 155 out. I will add some more speed above the target speed. Well, everything else is all right. In case of go-around, since it is VFR, while staying visual and turning to the right at... request a radar vector. If not, we have to go to FLAKE[10]... turn towards FLAKE... turning towards a course 062 outbound heading 242 and hold as published. Since the localiser glide slope is out, MDA is 560 feet and HAT is 304 feet. It was a little lengthy. This concludes my landing briefing.

The chief's explanations were punctuated by coughing fits that showed he was still suffering from his bout of bronchitis. Nevertheless, he did not make a short briefing as had been his stated intent. He simply botched it. Investigators later explained that his talk contained mistakes, was muddled and incomplete. He failed to give any information on certain essential safety parameters. They pointed out that a "non-precision" approach required much more specific groundwork than any other approach. So, although the Captain had briefly reminded his crew that the glide was not working, he gave no explanation as to how the approach was going to be made... He did not give the minimal descent altitudes and the only altitude he alluded to was in the wrong order. Neither did he mention the distances to be respected before starting the step-like descent along the runway axis. Nothing too was said about the weather. In addition, the Captain should have checked that the approach charts he was using were still valid. If he had done so, he would have realised that they were out of date by more than two months[11]. In fact, despite the numerous first person singulars he used, which served only to remind everybody that he was the sole master on board, Park Yung Chul's briefing was empty of content. Nothing was decided and instead of him and his subordinates being prepared for a complex approach nobody really knew how things were going to be addressed. Not even Park himself. This is a way short of the mark when you are in charge of a Jumbo jet carrying hundreds of passengers.

---

[10] FLAKE is an intersection point situated 7 nautical miles on radial 2".
[11] In many airlines, checking the date of the approach charts forms an essential element of the briefing.

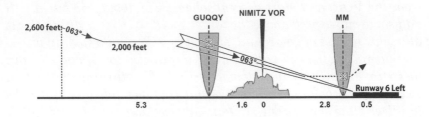

Vertical cross-section of the ILS approach

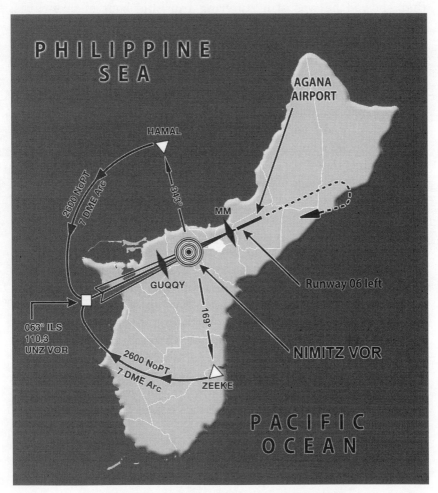

Schematic approach of Runway 06 Left's ILS

Besides, Captain Park had just said that they would start their descent when they were 155 miles from their destination[12]. Then, a few seconds later he seemed to have changed his mind.

01:13:33 (Captain): *We better start [the] descent.*
The First Officer was careful not to say anything about this turnaround. Ever respectful, he simply murmured:

01:13:35 (First Officer): *Yes.*

Along with everything else, he called the Guam radar centre to warn them they were descending. This was for information only and not a request for permission since the controller had already told them to do as they wished.

01:13:40 (First Officer): *Guam centre, Korean 801, leaving level 410 for 2,600 feet.*

01:13:44 (CERAP controller): *Korean 801, Roger.*

Note that this altitude of 2,600 ft was not assigned to the Boeing by chance. This was a safety ceiling. If the aircraft remained above it, it would be perfectly safe and would never fly into the Guam hills. Several peaks on the island are above 1,000 feet high; there is even one summit that reaches 1,442 feet to the south of the runway axis. The most problematic potential obstacle was Mount Nimitz, rising up just 643 feet, but right on Runway 06's axis on which the 747 was getting ready to land.
The aircraft started its descent and the crew got ready. On the CVR recording you can hear the seats sliding forward towards the instrument panel. And it was at this moment that the Captain made the first remark that showed how tired he really was.

01:20:01 (Captain): *If this round trip is more than 9 hours trip, we might get a little something. With 8 hours, we get nothing... 8 hours do not help us at all.*

To understand the meaning of this remark, you have to remember that the crews' flying times are strictly regulated. Anyone who goes over the authorised number of hours is systematically allocated

---

[12] During his briefing, the Captain spoke of 155 miles outbound. He should have used the word inbound.

additional rest time. The "little something" the Captain wanted was not a salary bonus as might be imagined: he just wanted a bit of extra rest time when he returned to Seoul.

The problem was that this rest time would only be granted under certain conditions. The Seoul-Guam return flight had to be more than 8 hours and if that was not the case, there would be no extra rest time and so no refreshing sleep. That was why Captain Park Yung Chul wanted just one thing: for this rotation to last as long as possible and 9 hours would be just perfect.

And then, as if what he had just said was not clear enough, he added in a tired voice:

01:20:20 (Captain): *They make us work to maximum, up to maximum...*

His subordinates did not respond. Total silence... They knew that the conversation was being recorded by the CVR. Criticising the airline openly was not a privilege granted to all. With Korean Air, a Captain like Park Yung Chul was untouchable but things were very different for a mere First Officer or Flight Engineer. They could be sacked on the slightest pretext.

So the Captain continued talking to himself:

01:20:28 (Captain): *Probably this way* (unintelligible words), *hotel expenses will be saved for cabin crews... And maximise the flight hours. Anyway, they make us B747 classic guys work to maximum[13].*

This was bitter criticism indeed. The Captain was explaining straight and to the point that the airline was exploiting them. As far as he was concerned, it would be healthier to let the crews sleep in Guam instead of getting them to fly back to Seoul in the middle of the night.

Then, to make things clearer, he yawned:

01:20:35 (Captain): *Oh... really... feel like sleeping.*

It was the middle of the night and the most difficult moment of the trip for Park Yung given the jet lag accumulated from the other

---

[13] The airline had two sectors for its Boeing 747s:
- The older types 200 and 300; these were the "Classics"
- The more recent 400 series which were part of a separate sector and more privileged.

flight rotations. The whole sequence of events here led to him being at his sleepiest just as the aircraft was about to commence the most difficult phase of its approach. His capacity for concentration was greatly reduced in these circumstances. And it was just then that the First Officer gave him a report on the weather they were going to run into on Guam.

01:21:59 (First Officer): *Captain, Guam condition is no good.*

However, the First Officer's still respectful tone failed to elicit a response[14] and Park Yung Chul did not even ask to be informed on the conditions prevailing at Guam. He just looked at the weather radar that revealed rain along their route. Zones in red appeared at that moment on their screen. These were the storm cells into which even a Boeing 747 could not venture. These contain hail, strong turbulence and vertical winds powerful enough to break up any aircraft. They had to head for the green-coloured zones.

After a long moment of thought, Park announced in a barely audible voice.

01:22:26 (Captain): *It's raining heavily.*

Again silence… Hesitation… Then faced with the sheer size of the areas of rainfall, he decided to make a turn to avoid the storms. He spoke to the First Officer for him to call the CERAP controller.

01:23:45 (Captain): *Request 20 miles deviation later on.*

Initially, the First Officer answered as usual, briefly and submissively.

01:23:47 (First Officer): *Yes.*

But when he examined the radar, he could not help noting that his boss's instructions were lacking in sagacity.

01:24:05 (First Officer): *Don't you think it rains more? In this area?*

---

[14] In most airlines a First Officer would not speak to his boss as "Captain" but use his first name instead (even if it was the first time he was flying with him). In French-speaking countries, the use of the familiar "tu" form is even de rigueur.

No matter how respectful his tone, he was challenging the Captain's authority. Despite his tiredness, Park's reply was like a whiplash.

01:24:04 (Captain): *Left! Request deviation.*

Then, as Park was far from stupid, he re-considered, thinking that perhaps his First Officer's comment was justified. So he deftly corrected himself.

01:24:09 (Captain): *10 miles.*

01:24:10 (First Officer): *Yes.*

He carried out his boss's new order

01:24:30 (First Officer calling controller): *Guam centre… Korean 801, request deviation 10 miles left of track.*

01:24:35 (Controller): *0-1 approved.*

01:24:36 (Captain): *Thank you.*

Note in passing that the controller muddled his distance figures a little here. He should have said 1 – 0 to confirm 10 nautical miles. Nothing too serious: the crew understood perfectly well that they were cleared to make a detour of 10 nautical miles away from the route to their destination.

During the minutes that followed, the three men discussed the weather conditions on Guam. These were irregular. Certain sectors were saturated by enormous storm cells, others were perfectly clear. Everything depended on how the situation was going to develop. Cumulonimbi developed rather unpredictably and nobody could forecast where they would be when the aircraft landed.
A few moments later, the crew started the "approach checklist" but the First Officer had to break off at once. The 747 was passing through two cumulonimbus formations that were creating severe turbulence. Luckily, the aircraft was exactly in the centre of a clear corridor. The 10 nautical mile deviation was justified and it was evident that the First Officer had been right in not wanting to move too far off the route.
No praise for him was forthcoming from the Captain.

The Boeing came out of the storm zone a minute later and turbulence ceased. Everything now seemed to be clear and the Flight Engineer could not help showing how satisfied he was since they could now see a bright halo in the distance.

01:27:58 (Flight Engineer): *Today... weather radar has helped us a lot.*

01:27:53 (Captain): *Yes, it's very useful.*

The controller then gave them a heading to the right so that the aircraft could get back on course and the First Officer called a few seconds later to inform him that they had passed the danger zone.

01:31:17 (First Officer): *Guam Centre, Korean 801 clear of Charlie Bravo request radar vector for runway 6 left.*

01:31:31 (Controller): *Roger, Korean 801 fly heading 120.*

01:31:34 (First Officer): *Heading 120... Korean 801.*

The crew resumed going through the approach checklist. Lights were turned on, instruments checked, radio-altimeters connected, and shoulder harnesses put in place and tightened.
Then once again, the Captain examined the radar and noticed another red patch on the screen, another threatening storm cloud.

01:34:05 (Captain): *Yeah... there is a big CB[15] over there on the left.*

The Flight Engineer immediately became worried. The aircraft was only 18 miles from Guam and if this storm moved closer to the airport it could really cause them some problems.

01:34:23 (Flight Engineer): *Is it going to be rough?*

01:34:34 (Captain): *It may be better at lower altitude.*

In fact, as the aircraft advanced, the crew realised that the storm was not going to be a problem. They could start preparing the landing.

---

[15] CB for Cumulonimbus (storm clouds).

01:38:37 (Captain): *Flaps 10.*

01:38:37 (First Officer): *Yes sir, flaps 10 degrees.*

The aircraft levelled out at 2,800 ft and pursued its approach with radar assistance. It was the controller who gave the headings and the crew carried out the instructions. At first, Guam Centre asked the aircraft to veer off to the left on heading 090 (see illustration). The aim was to bring them gradually onto the localiser for Runway 06 Left. Remember that the instrument landing system was only partly operational. The crew could therefore acquire a position on the runway axis but they had no information about the approach glide path.

To come down safely in these conditions, the crew had to watch the distance in relation to the runway using the information supplied by the DME[16]. It could only descend without any risk once it had flown over the hills on the runway axis.

However, the Captain failed to mention this procedure during his briefing... From what distance could they descend safely? What steps would they have to take?

Nothing had been resolved!

Everybody knew however that the glide was out of use and in case anyone had forgotten, the controller reminded them once more.

01:39:44 (Guam controller): *Korean 801, cleared for ILS Runway 06 Left approach... glide slope unusable.*

01:39:48 (First Officer): *Korean 801, Roger... cleared ILS Runway 06 Left.*

Surprisingly, the First Officer did not read back the fact that the glide was out of use. Was this due to negligence, bad reception or just an oversight? Whatever it was, nobody could be certain that the crew was still aware of the failure. The following conversation did little to dispel any remaining doubts.

The only one who seemed to remember was the Flight Engineer and he spoke to confirm the information:

01:39:55 (Flight Engineer): *Is the glide slope working? Glide slope? Yeah?*

---

[16] Distance Measuring Equipment: a system giving the distance of the aircraft in relation to the VOR beacon.

01:39:55 (Captain): *Yes, yes it's working!*

What explanation can be given for this strange response? Truly exhausted, he seemed to be out of touch with reality. The controller had reminded them barely ten seconds earlier that the system was out of use and then the Captain said the opposite... This time, the matter was so serious that the First Officer and Flight Engineer dared to intervene, albeit mildly and very politely.

01:39:59 (Flight Engineer): *Ah, so...*

01:39:59 (Unidentified): *Check the glide slope if working?*

01:39:59 (probably the Captain): *Why? Is it working?*

01:40:00 (First Officer): *Not usable...*

Finally, it was the First Officer who spoke up, but his words were lost in the general conversation. Everybody was talking at once. The result now was that the aircraft was on the runway axis but it still remained unclear as to whether the Captain was aware that the glide was out of service. They were now getting closer to the ground. Six seconds later, the 747 reached 2,600 ft. This was the minimum altitude set by the CERAP controller. The distance in relation to the runway now had to be monitored and the runway approached in successive steps.
But how could anyone proceed to carry out a procedure that had not been mentioned in the briefing?
Then suddenly, as the aircraft was established on the final approach, an unidentified voice insisted!

01:40:22 (Unidentified voice): *Glide slope is incorrect.*

The person having just spoken was either the First Officer or the Flight Engineer. It cannot have been the Captain because, had it been him, he would have given instructions to modify the procedure. At that moment, one of the two subordinates probably tried discreetly get the Captain to grasp the fact that they were making a huge mistake: this was no way to follow an approach without the glide... The controller had signalled it, the First Officer had repeated it and one crew member repeated it several times over...

At last Park Yung Chul seemed to hesitate.

01:40:33 (Captain): *Since today's glide slope condition is not good, we need to maintain 1,440 feet. Please, set it.*

This was indeed a strange formulation! "Glide slope condition is not good". This suggests the system was seen to be underperforming or only working intermittently, but that it could nevertheless be used. But this was not at all the case... and in such conditions they were heading for a disaster.

The aircraft was now on the runway axis, lined up on the localiser and at an altitude of 2,200 feet (see illustration). Straight ahead of it was Mount Nimitz standing at 643 feet. All that was needed was for the crew to follow the "without glide" approach for everything to go smoothly. First they would have to fly over the hill and then set a controlled descent respecting the altitudes in relation to the distance to be covered. Not that complicated although it did mean being much more careful than for a classic ILS approach.

While things remained indecisive in the cockpit, the controller continued watching the approach on his radar. His work would be over once the aircraft was 9.3 miles from the runway. At that moment the crew would change frequency to switch over to contact with the control tower.

01:40:42 (Controller): *Korean Air 801, contact the Agana control tower on 118.10... Ahn nyung hce ga sae yo ("good bye" in Korean).*

Flattered to hear an American controller speaking Korean, the First Officer replied immediately in his own language.

01:40:47 (First Officer): *Soo go ha sip si yo ("take care" in Korean). 118.10.*

01:40:50 (Flight Engineer, amused): *The guy working here was probably a GI in Korea before.*

01:40:52 (Captain glumly): *Yes.*

As the frequency had already been prepared on the VHF 2 radio, the First Officer immediately contacted the tower as requested.

01:40:55 (First Officer): *Agana Tower, Korean Air 801, intercept the localiser 06 left.*

01:41:01 (Agana Tower): *Korean 801 "heavy"... Agana Tower Runway 06 Left. Wind... 090 at 7 knots... cleared to land. Verify heavy Boeing 747 tonight.*

In fact, the controller wanted to check that it was not the usual Airbus 300 but the First Officer seemed not to understand the question and made no reply:

01:41:14 (First Officer): *Korean 801 Roger... cleared to land Runway 06 Left.*

The countdown had now begun. The aircraft was only 8 miles from the runway. The flaps were down 30° and it was time to do the landing checklist. At that moment, visibility was extremely variable. From time to time, the 747 would come out of the clouds and the crew could see the glow of the town in the distance. Then, it would go through a rainy area again with the windshield clouding over and zero visibility.

01:41:18 (Captain): *Look carefully for...*

The Captain was clearly asking his subordinates to seek out the runway lights. But this was pointless. Outside, it was pitch black! The aircraft passed through 1,500 ft and continued to go down blindly. The Captain seemed to have forgotten that they weren't to go below 1,440 ft under any circumstances.
The order he then gave was to have dire consequences:

01:41:33 (Captain): *Set 560 feet.*

The situation suddenly took an absolutely incredible turn. The Boeing was over very uneven terrain and the Captain had just decided to descend into the hills without taking the most elementary precautions. Worse... The aircraft was heading straight to the VOR beacon which was right on top of Mount Nimitz. At 643 feet, it was the highest point on the flight path and the altitude limit had just been set at 560 feet! All this could only end badly. And it was at this moment that the Captain asked in a tired voice:

01:41:46 (Captain): *Isn't glide slope working?*

There was no response from the crew members. They clearly were at a loss to understand what was going on... because once again the question was ludicrous. The only possible explanation is that Park's state of exhaustion was not just physical but that his intellectual capacity was also severely affected. How otherwise can one interpret the fact that after the subject of the "out-of-order glide" had been brought up so many times, the man should still have been asking whether the system was operational or not? It would have been comical but for the lives of the 254 passengers hanging on a thread...

It remains astonishing that neither the First Officer nor the Flight Engineer reacted. They had heard and they knew there was a big risk of it not working. Did this absolute respect they had for their Captain prevent them from speaking up and saying that they were all in danger of being killed?

The crew's attention was then drawn to another event of much lesser import: the aircraft had just gone into another rain zone. As the drops pattered on the windshield once again the Captain ordered:

01:41:48 (Captain): *Wiper on!*

01:41:49 (First Officer): *Yes, wiper on.*

The wipers could be heard rapidly scraping the windshield. Then, clearly ill-at-ease, the First Officer asked:

01:41:59 (First Officer): *Not in sight?*

Nobody answered because the runway lights could still not be seen... At that moment the aircraft was at 1,100 feet. It was under the safety height and no longer protected from running into the hills. At that moment the GPWS[17] alarm sounded.

01:42:00 (GPWS Synthetic voice): *500 (feet)!*

At that very moment, the Flight Engineer was unable to hold back a cry of surprise. He was the quickest to react and you could hear a note of anguish:

---

[17] Ground Proximity Warning System.

01:42:02 (Flight Engineer): *Eh?*

Clearly something was seriously wrong... The unusual difference between the figures supplied by the altimeter and the alarm that had just been triggered was blatant. The immediate thing to do was pull up. Not to speculate and re-start the breakthrough from the beginning. As the Captain remained impassive, somebody blurted out a warning. There is no way of knowing whether this was the First Officer or the Flight Engineer:

01:42:03 (Unidentified voice): *Stabilise, stabilise.*

01:42:04 (Captain): *Oh, yes...*

That was all... But nothing was done to level off. There was not the slightest action and no attempt was made to return to the safety altitude. The descent continued and the aircraft came ever closer to the hills.
And the crew carried on reading the "landing" checklist as if nothing was untoward was happening:
   - Auto-brake connected to minimum.
   - The three green gear lights checked.
   - The speed brakes armed.
   - "No smoking" signal on.
And then, as this bout of questions and answers went on, another voice alarm was sounded. This was the GPWS and it was even more worrying than before:

01:42:11 (GPWS Synthetic voice): *Minimums... Minimums...*

Nobody reacted even though this alarm meant that the aircraft was going down past the minimum breakthrough altitude. The radio-altimeter interpreted this loss of altitude as a final approach to the runway and the Captain was making the same deduction. The problem was that the runway was still 3¾ miles away and that the aircraft was 840 feet above sea level skimming the hilltops. If the scene had occurred in daytime the crew would have jumped at the throttles.
Note that in the control tower the controller too failed to react, for the good reason that his radar told him nothing. In fact the MSAW

system was not operational at Guam[18]. This system would have enabled the radar to sound an alarm if the aircraft was flying over obstacles. Unfortunately, for some unknown reason, the American administration on Guam had recently had the software modified and the alarm was no longer operational.

The 747 therefore continued to descend gently towards the hills and the crew continued their checklist as if everything was normal:
  - Hydraulics checked.
  - Lights on.

The 747's rate of sink[19] was 1,400 feet per minute. Naturally, since the obstacles were so close, the GPWS estimated that this was too fast. Once again, it set off its alarm.

01:42:19 (GPWS Synthetic voice): *Sink rate!! Sink rate!!*

This time, fear suddenly invaded the cockpit. Again the first person to react was the Flight Engineer who gave the alarm first.

01:42:19 (Flight Engineer): *200 feet!*

As was only to be expected, his voice was strained. The aircraft was still a long way from the runway and it was rumbling along just 200 feet above the ground! All this information was contradictory. It was the First Officer who quite surprisingly reacted the most logically. In spite of the immense respect his Captain inspired in him, he dared to make a suggestion.

The tone of his voice betrayed his sense of worry:

01:42:19 (First Officer): *Let's make a missed approach.*

Nothing could be have been wiser... They were 100 feet from the ground, still 3½ nautical miles from the runway and it was pitch black in front of the windshield. Not the least airport light in sight! As Park Yung Chul remained motionless, the Flight Engineer insisted gravely.

01:42:20 (Flight Engineer): *Not in sight!*

---

[18] Minimum Safe Altitude Warning: a radar alarm system that warns the controller when an aircraft flies too low over obstacles.

[19] The rate by which the aircraft drops towards the ground.

Still no reaction from the left-hand seat as the 747 continued to descend. It was now 680 feet above sea level but the fuselage was about to touch the rocks.
So the First Officer added, pointedly:

01:42:21 (First Officer): *Not in sight! Missed approach.*

Still no reaction from the Captain. The Flight Engineer insisted.

01:42:22 (Flight Engineer): *Go around!*

The First Officer now took things into his own hands. He grasped the column and started to pull gently. It was only now that the Captain decided to say:

01:42:23 (Captain): *Go around!*

But it was too late. The 747 weighs more than 200 tons and just increasing the pitch attitude was not enough to make a go-around[20]. The aircraft pulled up gently but it still continued to descend with its nose in the air.
The GPWS carried on with its fateful countdown:

01:42:25 (GPWS Synthetic voice): *100 feet... 50...40... 30... 20...*

The CVR then recorded a succession of very violent blows amid which you could hear groans and screams.

01:42:32: the recording went dead. The aircraft had hit the top of Mount Nimitz at 190 mph. With the violence of the impact, it disintegrated and caught fire.

The crash occurred a few hundred yards from a man who was out night-hunting. The 747 first passed a couple of dozen feet over his head then headed straight into a rocky piton. The hunter explained later that it had been raining heavily until a few seconds earlier. Then, there had been a lull at the moment the Jumbo jet crashed. The stars were clearly visible.
From his position in the hills, the man could not see the beacons but he could clearly make out the lights of the town slightly to the left.

---

[20] The column moves back at a rate of one degree per second.

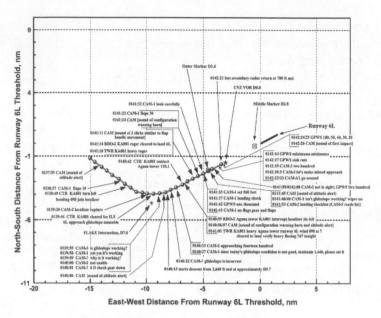

Horizontal section of the approach

Two and a half minutes after the accident, the controller called the 747.

01:45 (Guam Tower): *Agana Tower, Korean 801 heavy, do you receive me?*

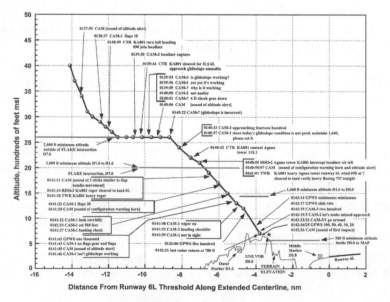

Vertical section of the approach

Obviously, nobody answered but at first the controller was unconcerned. The showers were heavy in the west and it was not unusual not to see the lights of incoming airplanes. He thought the crew was just concentrating on landing.

But four minutes later he called the "Follow me" vehicle whose task it was to escort the 747 to its disembarkation gate. What follows is the recording of the conversation between the tower and the driver[21]:

01:49 (Agana Tower): *Is Korean Air with you?*

01:49 (Driver of the "Follow me"): *Well, no!*

The controller tried to get in touch with the Jumbo Jet.

01:49 (Agana Tower): *Korean 801, Tower, how do you receive me?*

The controller received no reply but believed the 747 to be on the runway but hidden behind the heavy rain.

01:50 (Controller calling the vehicle): *Is it with you now?*

01:50 (Driver of the "Follow me"): *Nope!*

He made another fruitless attempt to get in touch with the Jumbo Jet.

01:50 (Agana Tower): *Korean 801, Tower, how do you read me?*

The controller called the vehicle back and the conversation continued between the two men:
"I don't understand. It was with me. I cleared it to land. I don't know where it's got to now… I didn't even see it."
"You never saw it?"
"Negative".
"But has it landed?
"Negative".
"Oh, my God!"
The controller was now deeply concerned and called the radar control of Andersen military base to ask whether the 747 had

---

[21] Whatever the origin all radio or telephone conversations to and from a control tower are systematically recorded.

landed there. The runways of the two aerodromes are parallel and the crew could have mistaken them, something that occurred fairly frequently[22].

As the answer was negative, he called the vehicle once again:
"I can't find it anywhere. The pilot called me, I allowed him to land... I've lost him."

Fearing for the worst, the controller called Flight Ryan International 789. This was a Boeing 727 cargo on its approach. The words of the Captain were chilling.

"Well, about fifteen minutes ago, we saw a bright red glow in the clouds. It was bit strange. We thought it was an optical effect."

And just as the pilot was coming for his final approach he added:
"Er, for your information, there's big fire on the side of the hill."

Astounded the controller called the "Follow me".

"The Ryan flight has just told me there's a fire on the other side of Nimitz Hill."

"A fire on the other side of Nimitz Hill?"

"Affirmative. It could be a crash..."

The Ryan International flight continued circling for some time over the sector giving information about the area's geographical co-ordinates. It was no longer raining and the glow of the fires was visible from afar.

It finally landed at 02:03 after which the airport was completely closed to traffic.

Runway 06 Left - Wreck

---

[22] See Erreurs de Pilotage Vol. 2 by the same author, published by Altipresse.

A surprising photo of the scene of the accident.
You can distinctly make out quite the Nimitz VOR beacon (in the middle of the round cement platform). In the distance only 5 miles away, Guam Airport's Runway 06 Left is also clearly visible.

View of the VOR beacon with the still-smoking wreck, eight hours after the crash

As sometimes happens in dramatic situations, there were scenes bordering on the burlesque. The aircraft had crashed onto territory occupied by the US Navy and the military authorities would not accept the idea of the civil administration seeking to direct operations there. Also, nobody knew who should be responsible for rescue operations: the island's Governor, the US Navy, the US Air Force, the US Coastguards or the airport authorities? It took time for the orders to come down from on high deciding who was to direct operations. Then there were problems of access. Nimitz Hill is only served by a narrow, sinuous road. In the crash, the 747 had torn up a pipeline on the side of the road and the debris from the mains prevented the rescue teams from advancing. The firemen's vehicles tried going round it but the earth was soaked and they got bogged down one after the other. The firemen therefore had to proceed on foot and it took two further hours to free the vehicles and get them to the scene of the tragedy.
Some eight hours after the crash, the fire from the burning wreck was still not under control.

Shortly afterwards, the American army sent hundreds of soldiers to search the debris. When they arrived on Mount Nimitz, no-one expected to find any survivors.

But quite unexpectedly, there were a few...

The tragedy caused 227 dead but there were 27 escapees, some of whom were wandering around in the rain. Most of them explained that their first vision at the moment of impact was that of the luggage lockers opening above their heads. Dozens of bags fell out on the floor which seemed to be disappearing at each instant. Then "fire burst out all over the place and spread at top speed throughout the cabin."

A woman sitting in row 34 later recalled seeing her husband suddenly engulfed in flames. "Then in a fraction of a second he disappeared."

Sitting in First Class, seat 3b, was Hyun Seong Hong, 36. He recalled that "everything happened in an instant". He was sitting peacefully when there was a terrible noise. The passengers did not have the time to shout. "It was like in a disaster film with all the special effects; then the aircraft suddenly disappeared from the décor around them." When he came round a few minutes later, he was lying in the wet grass. "It was just like daylight because there were flames everywhere."

One of the hostesses was sitting on the jump seat R1, up front. She said she heard a terrible noise which she later called a "big boom". She had no time to be scared as the aircraft just tore up all around her. In a few seconds, she was thrown out of the cabin and found herself in the rain still strapped to her jump seat. Without really understanding what had just happened to her, she unfastened her belt, went ten yards along a smoking partition and saw a passenger screaming. She rushed to help her.

Barry Small was a New Zealand helicopter pilot. At first, he thought that the 747 crew had missed its landing on the runway. But a ball of fire burst through the cabin. Passengers started screaming and disappearing in the middle of the flames. Barry then rushed to a tear in the fuselage and ran off. He later explained to the investigators that, according to him, the fire spread very rapidly because some bottles of spirits were badly battened down in the galleys. He decided to create an association whose aim was to modify the international regulations concerning the storage of alcoholic beverages aboard aircraft.

This decision was greeted with a certain amount of scepticism[23].

Then there was another miracle with young Rika Matsuda, an eleven year old South Korean[24]. She was travelling to the rear of the aircraft with her father Tatsuo and her mother Sung Yeo Cho. At the moment of the crash, the entire family was trapped under heaps of debris and luggage. However, being so small, she succeeded in slipping out from under her belt. She tried to help her mother escape, but the fire spread so quickly that she had to flee. Unharmed she found herself outside alone and began wandering in the rain for more than an hour. She ended up by coming across the hostess, Lee Yong Ho, with whom she sheltered under a tree and slept while waiting for the rescue teams. It was Carlos Gutierrez, the Governor of the island in person who found her. He and his wife took charge of the child at their home for more than a week.

Rika Matsuda returned to Korea a week later aboard a 747 like the one in the tragedy (see photo).

Young Rika Matsuda returning to Korea, only a week after the accident
(photo taken in the cockpit of a 747 similar to the one in the accident)

---

[23] The total quantity of spirits aboard a 747 represents thirty or so litres (mainly miniatures in the First Class cabin). This quantity is negligible compared with the tons of kerosene in the wing tanks.

[24] The child was first wrongly described as Japanese due to her living in Tokyo.

Captain Park Yung Chul, the First Officer and the Flight Engineer were not so lucky. They were killed instantly together with the 224 other occupants of the aircraft.

One can only note that this tragedy is a characteristic example of how a series of different factors accumulate and bring about an accident:

- The Captain was in a state of acute fatigue. His analytical capacity seemed very low. It is obvious that his mental and physical exhaustion was at the origin of the serious errors he committed.

- His undisputable authority prevented the First Officer and the Flight Engineer from taking control of the situation.

- The weather was very unstable. Although it was fine in some places, it was raining heavily in the northwest.

- The tragedy took place at night. A night approach is always more difficult to handle.

- The beginning of the flight was very agitated. Whatever the type of aircraft and no matter how experienced the crew, turbulence is always an extra stress and fatigue factor.

- The ILS was not fully operational. Only the localiser was working, while the glide was being serviced.

- The airport's Minimum Safe Altitude Warning (MSAW) system software was not operational; the controller could not tell the 747 of the danger it was in.

- Although this fact played no role in the accident, the aeronautical maps supplied by the airline were out of date.

A few days after the accident report was published, Sik Choon Park, Training Manager at Korean Air said: "I just can't understand *why* this happened." One of the investigators therefore told him that perhaps he ought to look more closely into the fact that in his airline, neither a First Officer nor a Flight Engineer could question decisions made by a Captain.
The airline finally decided to change its procedures. In the event of imminent danger, a First Officer would now have the right to take over the controls if the Captain failed to respond after two suggestions to pull up had been made. This procedure nevertheless remained highly theoretical. Two years after these events, a Boeing 747 from the same airline crashed at Stansted because the First Officer dared not contradict his Captain[25].

---

[25] Read Erreurs de Pilotage N°3 (Story: "Silence fatal") by the same author, published by Altipresse.

Following this accident, Korean Air management decided to suspend their flights to Guam. This was a strange reaction that had severe repercussions on the island's tourist industry as also as on the airline's revenues. This retaliatory measure lasted for four years before management realised that everyone was losing out and flights were then resumed[26].

This was not the first accident involving a pilot suffering from exhaustion:

- On 27 July 1989, a Korean Air DC-10 crashed at Tripoli in very similar conditions to those on Guam, with no glide and poor weather condition. The Libyan crash investigators raised the issue of crew fatigue.
- On 1 April 1991, a Tropical Air Service aircraft crashed after the pilot had gone beyond the regulation flying time by 41 hours 30 minutes[27].
- On 18 August 1993, a DC-8 belonging to the Kalitta airline crashed on the base at Guantanamo. The crew had been working for 18 hours non-stop without the slightest rest period.
- On 29 April 1993, Flight Continental Express 2733 crashed in Arkansas after the crew had worked for three days and made seven flights without any rest over the previous 24 hours.

This tragic event was followed by one of the most appalling swindles ever. Just a few days after the accident, some Nigerian-based crooks used the names of the victims to create websites purportedly collecting funds for the victims' families. The scam was so well designed that generous Korean donators were taken in and money flooded in. The Guam government had to intervene to close down some of these sites but unfortunately the crooks were never brought to justice and neither were the embezzled funds ever recovered.

---

[26] The Seoul-Guam route is now served by Airbus 330-200s and 330-300s. Departure is no longer from Gimpo Airport but from "Incheon International Airport".

[27] See "CHARTER Pour ne plus voyager en mauvaises compagnies", by the same author published by Altipresse.

Stall! Stall! Stall!

This accident and the mystery surrounding it aroused considerable emotion in France and Brazil. For nearly two years, the world tried to understand what happened to Flight AF 447. Many theories were concocted, most of which focused on the failure of the Airbus's Pitot tubes and few people imagined that the whole disaster could be ascribed to mere pilot error. It was only when the flight recorders were finally recovered nearly 2½ miles (3,900 m) beneath the surface of the sea that the truth finally came.

Beyond the questions it raised about modern flight safety and pilot training, the Rio-Paris Crash will remain a textbook case in the annals of air transport.

The Airbus 330-200 in this narrative (registration F-GZCP)

1 June 2009

Air France has for long been one of the most prestigious airlines in the world, maybe even *the* most prestigious. It has flown legendary aircraft like the Concorde and the Super Constellation. Those French pilots who in the past flew the Atlantic were exceptional men. In the trade, they were referred to as *les Seigneurs* (the Lords) because every flight they made was something of an adventure, always an exploit of sorts. Navigation required extraordinary skills. They had to continue calculating the route all the time, struggle against the weather and resolve fuel problems. Few people know that, until recently, there was still an astrodome on some of the airlines' Boeing 707s; this was a sort of transparent dome located above the cockpit that enabled the pilot to navigate using the stars by means of a sextant and regulate gyroscopic drift!

Nowadays all that has disappeared and navigation is no longer a problem. The airlines' aircraft are equipped with the most sophisticated systems. At the touch of a key, the computer immediately supplies all the vital data and the aircraft are easy to fly, even forgiving many of the mistakes pilots may make. The result is that training methods have changed. Dare we say it? They are much less complex. It would seem a total waste of time to study cosmography since the aircraft already knows the route it is taking and needs no prompting. The problem is that in some conditions nowadays modern pilots can be nonplussed by a minor breakdown which would have just brought a smile from the veterans.

A COMMERCIAL SUCCESS: THE AIRBUS 330-200

On this 1 June 2009, the aircraft operating the Rio-Paris route was an Airbus 330-200 registered F-GZCP. It was a recent aircraft since it was only 4 years old. It had never had an accident and like all Air France aircraft had been maintained according to an extremely rigorous protocol.

Even though the A330 was not the manufacturer's leading model, it was nonetheless a fine commercial success. At the time of writing, 1,155 examples have been sold and 90 airlines operate it all around the world. Year in year out, the Airbus 330 has proved itself to be remarkably reliable since only three machines have ever been involved in accidents and no crash has raised doubts as to the airplane's reliability[1]. It remains a favourite with the pilots who often prefer it to the 340 which is heavier and does not perform quite so well.

To better understand the sequence of events that took place on this Rio-Paris flight you need to know some details on how an Airbus functions.

---

[1] A balance accident during the prototype's test flights (June 1994), a terrorist attack (July 2011) and pilot error (May 2010).

FLY-BY-WIRE CONTROLS

Unlike most conventional airliners, Airbuses are equipped with fly-by-wire flight controls. Thanks to these highly advanced systems, pilots fly the aircraft using a computer. On a conventional aircraft, there is direct human intervention on the controls and if a false move is made, the action is passed on to the machine with all the risks that entails. Nothing like that can happen with an Airbus because the computer would refuse to obey, acting like a kind of guardian angel preventing the aircraft from getting into a dangerous position (for instance the aircraft cannot bank, dive or climb beyond certain critical levels). But this protection is not used on all occasions. Depending on the circumstances, the aircraft can be piloted in three quite distinct modes:

"**Normal**" **Control Law**. This is the most frequently used mode: the computer manages the controls completely and operates the protective system that corrects potential pilot induced errors. If a pilot pulls right down on the stick at full speed or reduces power brutally while cruising, the aircraft will not obey as the software considers that the action might damage the airframe or cause the aircraft to stall. Thus, banking by more than 67 degrees is prohibited and a pitch attitude of more than 19 degrees will not be accepted as this could lead to the aircraft stalling. This flying mode is obviously extremely reassuring.

"**Alternate**" **Control Law**: this is a middle-of-the-road position. The aircraft can switch to this mode when it encounters unusual conditions, for example strong turbulence, or if it receives inconsistent data. In this case the computer continues to monitor the aircraft but some of the protection systems are inhibited. The guardian angel only decides to intervene in order to enable the pilot to resolve a problematic situation (which is what happened during the Rio-Paris flight).

"**Direct**" **Command Law:** this mode of flying has no protection element at all and is used when the aircraft is the victim of multiple failures. In this case, the guardian angel does not intervene and the controls are just like those on an ordinary aircraft: all the pilot's moves have an immediate effect on the airplane's behaviour.
In "Direct" law, the Airbus is just like any other aircraft!

Instrument panel on an A330-200. Starting in the centre of the photo there are three distinct types of screen:
- The two central screens are reserved for controlling the engines
- The two Navigational Display screens are in the middle part. They show the aircraft's flight path and the route followed with the different reporting points.
- The two Primary Flight Display screens are on the outer part of the photo. They show the artificial horizon, speed, the Mach number, the variometer, etc. It was this screen that the First Officers of the Airbus used when the Autopilot was disconnected.

What first strikes you when you look at the cockpit of an Airbus 330 (or any other Airbus for that matter as they are all alike), is how clear the instrumentation is. Everything is set out in an intuitive way and it takes a beginner just a few seconds to understand how it works. The manufacturer worked on a concept based above all on simplicity and ergonomics. Gone are the dozens of analogue dials with tiny needles. The information provided is easily readable and everything has been studied so that the Captain of a small Airbus A319 can take the controls of an enormous A 380 without having any problem adapting.
Everything is similar.

"JOYSTICKS"

The crew do not dispose of the two conventional big "steering wheel columns" but rather two small sticks located on the side consoles along the partition. These "joysticks" do not act on the controls but rather feed instructions into a computer that analyses the pilot's demands (as with pull up, dive or bank) and then applies them.

As a result, unlike the columns on a Boeing, the two "joysticks" do not move together when a pilot uses his controls. They can be used in three different ways:

- One of the pilots uses his joystick while the other leaves his stick alone. This is what happens in the vast majority of cases: the activated joystick sends the information to the flight calculator and the other remains inactive.

- Both pilots activate their joysticks at the same time. This is a "Dual Input" situation. In this case, it will be the algebraic sum of the action on the joysticks that prevails (the computer calculates the "average" of the pilots' movements). If one pilot pushes his stick full forward and the other pulls it as far back as possible the signals will cancel each other out and the aircraft will not change pitch. This type of situation is obviously very rare but "Dual Input" situations did occur during the last minutes of the Rio-Paris flight.

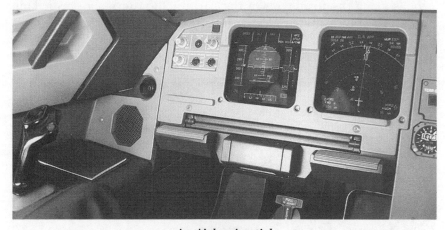

An Airbus joystick
You can make out the red pushbutton for taking priority over the other pilot.

- One of the pilots asserts his authority and decides to take priority over the other. To do so, he can press a red pushbutton located on his stick for three seconds. This sets off a sound and visual alarm warning that one of the sticks is "dead". If this does not suit the other pilot, he can countermand the order by doing the same thing. This strange "rivalry" also occurred several times during the Rio-Paris flight.

PITOT PROBES

Ever since Flight AF 447 went down in the Atlantic, a lot has been said about the anemometric probes. Before trying to describe what happened that night, it will be useful to give some details on these systems that are fitted to all aircraft in the world without exception.

In an aircraft, the speed in relation to the air is measured thanks to a probe placed on the fuselage. This is a tube that captures the pressure of the relative wind rushing into its tip. It was invented by French physicist Henri Pitot back in 1732. At the time it was used to measure the speed of flow of rivers. Today, as a tribute to their inventor, the probes on aircraft are still called Pitot tubes. The faster the aircraft moves, the higher will be the air pressure inside the tube. This pressure is measured by a capsule/sensor, the speed is deduced and then displayed on the instrument panel.

For greater safety, the manufacturer installs several anemometric probes along the fuselage. On the Airbus 330 there are three. One for the Captain's instrument panel, another for the First Officer's plus a spare one[2]. They are always placed near the nose of the aircraft in order to avoid the turbulence caused by the air flow.

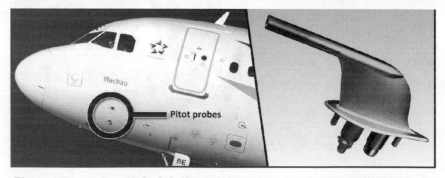

The two Pitot tubes on the left (Captain's and spare) are clearly visible on the front of this Airbus 320.

---

[2] The Captain's probe and the spare probe are located on the left of the fuselage, the First Officer's on the right.

The probe is an instrument that has no moving parts. As its name (Pitot tube) suggests, it is a tube with a tiny hole in the front part. The system has the advantage of never breaking down mechanically.

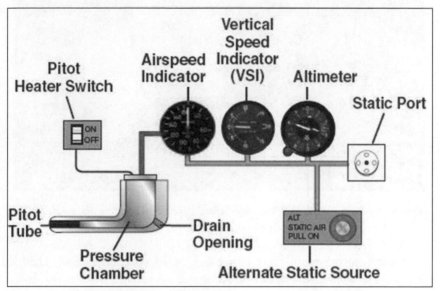

How the Pitot tube works based on a very simple principle

The only thing that prevents a probe from working is if something blocks the air intake. So, when an aircraft is grounded for a long time, the mechanics take special care to protect the Pitot tubes with cloth covers (the famous red "remove before flight" pennants) that prevent dust from entering them. The risk is very real. In January 1996, a Boeing 757 operated by Birgenair crashed with its 189 passengers on board because the protective covers had not been put on for several nights. The investigators discovered that flies had laid their eggs inside the tubes putting the probes out of action[3].

Flies are not the only things that can obstruct a Pitot tube. Splashes of mud, plant debris, sand and dust can all block the air intake. Another parameter that has to be taken into account is human absent-mindedness or oversights, with problems of adhesive tape, aircraft being painted without respecting the rulebook or even pilots taking off with the "Remove before flight" covers floating in the slipstream. These mistakes have sometimes had dire results, even resulting in crashes.

---

[3] See POURQUOI ILS SONT TOMBES by Jean-Pierre Otelli, published by Altipresse.

On this stationary jet, the "Remove before Flight" protective sheaths can be seen on the different Pitot tubes.

The last phenomenon that can block a Pitot tube is ice. This is the most frequently encountered problem with Pitot tubes since aircraft flying very high are subjected to very low temperatures (in the region of −55°). When the aircraft goes through a humid atmosphere, ice can cover certain exposed surfaces. To avoid this problem, a heating element is fitted inside the Pitot tube (see diagram). As soon as the weather conditions become critical, the crew switches on the Pitot heater system so as to stop ice forming and blocking the air intake.

Frost and ice are lethal dangers. An aircraft trying to take off in these conditions would crash immediately.

The Rio-Paris ROSTER

Flight AF447 flies the route between Rio de Janeiro and Paris Charles de Gaulle. For Air France crews this is a much sought-after trip. The Brazilian megalopolis is well known for its festive attractions and is therefore a popular destination, all the more so in so far as the scheduling is advantageous: the crew of Flight AF 447 left Paris on Thursday 28 May, returning from Rio on Sunday 31 May at 22.00, meaning a three-day stopover. The trip is so attractive that crew members are often accompanied by their spouses who can take advantage of the free flights granted family members by the airline.

The CREW

The flight lasts 10 hours 40 minutes[4]. The regulations therefore requir that at least three pilots be present aboard. There is a provision whereby each crew member is able to rest continuously for at least an hour and a half. So, on that night, apart from the Captain there were two First Officers who took it in turns in the cockpit depending on how tired they felt. It was the Captain who was to decide who had a break and when.

To sleep the crew disposes of a couchette just behind the flight deck[5]. In an emergency, those in control can call the man resting with a "High-Low Chime"[6] whose "Flight Rest" call button is located on the ceiling of the cockpit. The other less conventional method often used by crews is just to knock on the partition.

The Captain

The Captain was Marc D, aged 58. He had 11,000 flying hours to his credit. He was an airline pilot but also someone who had made it up the hard way. Marc D was one of those who had fought hard to realise their dream. He had first been a steward for Air France for

---

[4] For the Rio-Paris trip, the flight duty time was in fact 12 hours and 45 minutes, flight duty beginning as from the moment the crew turned up to prepare for the flight.

[5] In fact, there were two couchettes.

[6] A call comprising two tones, treble and bass, rather like normal door chimes.

six long years before going through a laborious training programme enabling him to obtain all his licences and qualifications: private pilot, instructor, qualification for mountain flying, demonstration pilot, professional pilot 1st Class and eventually airline transport pilot.

Marc D was originally recruited by Air Inter where he worked for almost nine years. It was only when that airline merged with Air France that he was incorporated into the prestigious flag carrier.

At the beginning of his career, Marc D flew all types of aircraft, including smaller ones like the Cessna 177, twin-turboprops like the Mitsubishi MU2 or the Nord 262 and more complex aircraft to fly like the Caravelle or Boeing 737-200. These aircraft disposed of very little automation and required particularly skilful piloting. As a result, Marc D was someone who had done a lot of mental calculations and many manual flying hours. While on this subject, some details about what is meant exactly by "flying hours". Nowadays, it no longer means hours "piloting an aircraft", far from it. The automation on modern aircraft is so sophisticated that we estimate that the pilot of, say, the Rio-Paris trip, spends only 8 to 9 minutes actually flying the aircraft manually. This very short time will be shared between take-off and landing, and the pilot has to be the "PF"[7], which is obviously not always the case. So, as already stated, Marc D had gone up through the ranks the old fashioned way. He had flown on light airplanes sometimes not even equipped with an Autopilot. All that made for an experienced pilot. We shall see shortly that this was not the case for one of his First Officers.

Note that, during his career, the Captain had trained with Air Inter on stalling Airbus 300s and he had done the same type of training on A320s with Air France, as well as training for piloting on Alternate Control Law and Direct Control Law with that type of aeroplane. He had also undergone training in conditions with dubious indicated speeds.

For that night's flight, Marc D was sitting in the left-hand seat on take-off but was PNF. He was therefore the one who dealt with the radio communications with the Brazilian controllers. At two in the morning, he decided to leave the flight deck and take a rest on the couchette. He returned only when the situation had already seriously deteriorated.

---

[7] "Pilot Flying" (the one in control of the aircraft) as opposed to Pilot Non-Flying (the one seeing to radio communications). The functions are exchanged regularly between the different crew members.

The "PNF" First Officer

This was David R. He was 37 and had logged 6,500 flying hours. During the last phase of the flight, he was sitting in the left-hand seat normally used by the Captain. He was apparently a brilliant element since he had been accepted for the competitive entrance exams to the ENAC. There are a variety of courses in France enabling you to become an airline pilot, but the one that ends with the Ecole Nationale de l'Aviation Civile (ENAC) is the most prestigious. The specialists consider it to be the best way to start a career in aeronautics. Recruitment is by means of a competitive entrance exam where there are many candidates but few succeed[8]. A qualification from ENAC is a passport for a job in the world's top airlines, and especially Air France… Apart from his airline pilot's licence, David R had also been on a training course to become an engineer with French Air Traffic Control.
He was qualified on Airbus 320, 330 and 340 but also holder of a single-engine aircraft qualification. In his free time, he occasionally flew small leisure aircraft like the TB 10.
During the different courses he had been on to obtain his qualification on Airbus 320, David R had had a session during which he studied high angle of attack flying and stalling under "Alternate" control law.
David R knew the route he was flying that night very well since he had been qualified on Airbus 330s and had already done 39 rotations in the South American sector.

The "PF" First Officer

This was Pierre-Cedric B and he sat in the right hand seat for the whole flight. He was the one who flew the aircraft during the last two hours.
He was 32 and had logged 2,900 flying hours. Of the three men on the flight deck he had the least experience. His career profile was completely different to that of his colleagues on the flight. Things had been relatively easy for him because he was what they called an Air France "cadet". His pilot training had at first been mainly theoretical. He had been on a two-year course at an aeronautics

---

[8] On average there are 30-40 enrolments for up to more than a 1,000 applications.

school with a good reputation[9]. As candidates often enter these schools without ever having flown an aircraft, they first follow a beginner's flying course during which they learn how to fly. When they graduate from the school they hold the theory airline pilot's licence and have also done about 180 flying hours in the school[10] but most of them have only done one hour solo at night[11].

Air France then takes them on to pursue an 8-month course at its training centre. It was during this second period that Pierre-Cédric was prepared to work on the route.

Pierre-Cedric B was now qualified on Airbus 320, 330, and 340. During his qualification on Airbus 320, he studied Alternate Control Law piloting and the stall approach, with a demonstration of the stall warning, and trained for flying at dubious indicated speeds.

For this trip to Rio, Pierre-Cedric had brought along his wife Isabelle. The young woman, who was a physics teacher in a preparatory class, was sitting at the front of the aircraft. Before this flight, Pierre-Cedric had already done five rotations in the South America sector, but only one to Rio de Janeiro.

The CABIN CREW

The Airbus 330 operational manual requires there to be a minimum of five cabin crew. That night there were 9 Flight Attendants to look after the passengers during the trip: 7 women (including the Cabin Senior Director) and 2 men.

The PASSENGERS

Among the 216 passengers aboard the aircraft, there were 126 men, 82 women, 7 children and a baby. As was often the case with such flights, the clientele was extremely varied, comprising 34 nationalities among which there were mainly 72 French, 59 Brazilians and 26 Germans. Some passengers were major figures

---

[9] For a cadet, studies are free and the trainee is paid. Conditions on the Air France site: http://www.devenirpiloteairfrance.com/cadets.asp

[10] The school recommends they have at least 15 to 20 flying hours in an aero-club before going on the course but this is not compulsory.

[11] About 130 hours of dual control and 50 hours solo by night. For a trainee not selected as an Air France cadet, the cost of this course for two years would have been around 90,000 Euros.

from industry, politics or the arts. Thus, there was the Chairman of Michelin South America, a famous conductor, several members of the Brazilian parliament and even a Pretender to the throne of Brazil.

The BEGINNING of the FLIGHT

The aircraft took off from Rio at 22:29[12]. It was carrying more than 70 tons of fuel in its tanks and its weight was 232.8 tons, practically the maximum take-off weight[13].

For some time there was doubt as to the identity of the First Officer sitting in the right-hand seat at around midnight. However, the investigators were in no doubt as to his identity once they had listened to the CVR:
"This is Pierre-Cedric who is at the controls of Airbus in the right-hand seat as PF.
"Captain Marc D is sitting in the left-hand seat but he's not flying. He's only the PNF."
The two men were alone in the cockpit. Autopilot N°2 was operational and the auto-throttles were on. The second pilot David R was having his break in the couchette.
The aircraft levelled out at level 350...
At first, it followed the Brazilian coastline heading north, flew over the city of Salvador, then along a leg via Recife heading to "Rumba Point" located just near Joao Pessoa. For the time being, it was still over Brazilian territory. It was from Natal that the Airbus started flying out over the Atlantic. The route it followed would have it fly over the points "Femur", "Intol", "Salpu", "Oraro" and "Tasil" (see diagram), then past Dakar, along the Moroccan coast, Portugal, Spain and finally France. This was the classic route for transatlantic flights joining Brazil and Europe.
The total distance was 5,625 miles.

During the first part of the flight, the atmosphere in the cockpit was relaxed. The weather was no problem. Visibility was excellent and there were practically no clouds. The two crew members had just finished their dinner. They were talking about a piece of music

---

[12] All the times indicated in this text are "Zulu" universal.
[13] 233 tons.

heard on a walkman when a hostess came in to ask them if they needed anything.

Here is the transcription of the recording made by the CVR from 00:26 onwards[14].

00:26:20 (Hostess): *Everything okay?*

00:00 (First Officer Pierre-Cedric B): *Tutti va bene?*

Then addressing the Captain, who seemed not to have heard:

00:00:00 (Hostess): *Everything okay for you too?*

00:26:26 (First Officer Pierre-Cedric B answering instead of the Captain): *And us too!*

00:26:26 (Hostess): *Everything ok?*

00:26:27 (Captain who still had not heard): *What?*

00:26:29 (Hostess): *Everything ok? No coffee, no tea?*

00:26:31 (Captain): *All's well.*

00:26:34 (First Officer Pierre-Cedric B): *So, we'll be getting on, see you later.*

00:26:38 (Hostess): *Thanks.*

The two men continued to discuss the piece of music on the walkman. The First Officer seemed to appreciate the atmosphere since his only regret was rather unexpected:

---

[14] The transcript and translation of what followed was made faithfully using the crew members' words. Nothing has been censored. Certain conversations seem to be of a personal nature but cannot be considered to be so when they have a direct or indirect link to flying the aircraft. Moreover, it seemed to us essential to transcribe all the stall alarms that were given by the synthetic voice. Even if the repetition of the word "Stall" may seem excessive, it merely reflects the reality of what happened. This repetition is vital for a complete understanding of the facts. Besides, it reproduces the stressful atmosphere that gradually built up as the tragic events unfolded.

00:29:59 (First Officer right-hand seat): *All that's missing is the whisky!*

A few seconds later the Captain drew his finger along a line which went from one side of the Navigation Display screen to the other. The line was still a long way ahead of them, almost at "Salpu" Point (see diagram).

00:31:00 (Captain): *The equator... You understood, I suppose?*

00:31:00 (First Officer right-hand seat): *OK, I thought so.*

In fact, the First Officer had already done several transatlantic flights and it was not the first time he had crossed the equator, but crossing from one hemisphere to the other is still something which crews find moving, be they sailors or airmen. That was why the Captain purposely drew attention to it.

A few moments later the controller's voice sounded in the speakers:

00:32:24 (Recife controller): *Air France 459, Squawk Ident for control.*

The Captain replied at once.

00:32:29 (Captain): *Squawk Ident Air France 447.*

And at the same time he pressed the radar identification button on the transponder. This enabled the controller to spot him on his screen. This message unfortunately was not intended for the Airbus but for another Air France aircraft: AF Flight 459. Captain Marc D answered nevertheless.
The First Officer reacted immediately:

00:32:29 (First Officer): *That wasn't ours... Was that for us?*

00:32:32 (Captain): *Yes...*

Obviously the Brazilian controller failed to understand what was happening.
This identification had made an aircraft he was expecting appear on his screen. Flight AF 459 was on the Sao-Paolo – Paris route. It

was also an Airbus but it was twenty minutes behind Flight 447. The controller wanted to know more:

00:32:35 (Controller): *Air France 447. Listening.*

Somewhat ironically, the First Officer rectified:

00:32:39 (First Officer): *You see, it was Air France 459!*

So the Captain had to find a way to make the controller understand that he was mistaken:

00:32:41 (Captain): *Er... Air France 447. Squawk Ident...*

The controller was quick on the uptake despite it being late.

00:32:46 (Controller): *OK. Air France 447. Copied... Squawk Ident instead of Air France 459... Maintain level 350.*

To conclude the Captain decided to turn the misunderstanding into a joke.

00:32:48 (Captain): *We'll get there in the end... We'll get there in the end.*

From then on, the pilot of Flight 459 took over and it was he who sent the correct "Ident" signal enabling the Brazilian controller to spot him.
A few seconds later the Recife controller asked the Airbus to switch frequency onto 128.70 MHz and the Captain did so at once.

00:36:33 (Captain): *Recife. Air France 447. Good evening... Level 350...*

00:36:39 (Controller radar): *Air France 447, Good evening. Radar control. Maintain level 350 to "INTOL" intersection. Contact 6535 on HF and 5565 on the secondary frequency. Good night.*

00:36:58 (Captain): *6-5-3-5 and 5-5-6-5 for HF frequency... Air France 447.*

As required by the procedure, the Captain clearly repeated the frequencies on which he would soon have to call as expressed in kilohertz. These were important since VHF communication would shortly be inoperative[15]. They would have to use HF radio, the only one used for long hauls over the Atlantic.

But there was a problem. Marc D did not seem to have understood when he had to switch over to HF. He also seemed unwilling to call the controller back to have it repeated to him.

So he asked the First Officer:

00:37:10 (Captain): *Where? Towards which point did he say?*

00:37:14 (First Officer): *Ah that, I dunno… I didn't get it.*

At first, the crew refrained from inquiring any further. After all, they had plenty of time; for the moment the Airbus was still flying along the Brazilian coast and this change of frequency would only be needed once the aircraft was over the Atlantic. Up until now the aircraft had flown over the towns of Maceio, then Recife and "Rumba". It now carried on as scheduled towards the town of Natal, before heading out over the ocean with "Femur" and "Intol". Only once the aircraft had passed this last point would it have to change to the "Atlantico" HF frequency[16].

As far as the weather was concerned, there was still no problem. Visibility was perfect. Unfortunately this was not going to last all night as the aircraft was nearing the zone where an "ITF" was building up.

---

[15] The VHF range (Very High Frequency) is "optical". The higher the aircraft flies, the longer the range. But however powerful the transmitter is, there are limitations caused by the Earth's curvature. HF (High Frequency) waves have a greater range because they are reflected off the ionosphere. In general, the quality of communication is not as good as VHF. Reflection back from the ionosphere is more or less effective according to the position of the Sun.

[16] The geographical coordinates for the different reporting points are as follows:
RUMBA: S 07 07,3 / W 035 46.4
FEMUR: S 03 38.0 / W 034 02.2
INTOL: S 01 21.7 / W 032 49.9
SALPU: N 00 26.6 / W 031 52.6
ORARO: N 02 14.8 / W 030 55.4
TASIL: N 04 00.3 / W 029 59.4
Note that "Intol" is in the southern hemisphere whereas "Salpu" is in the northern hemisphere.

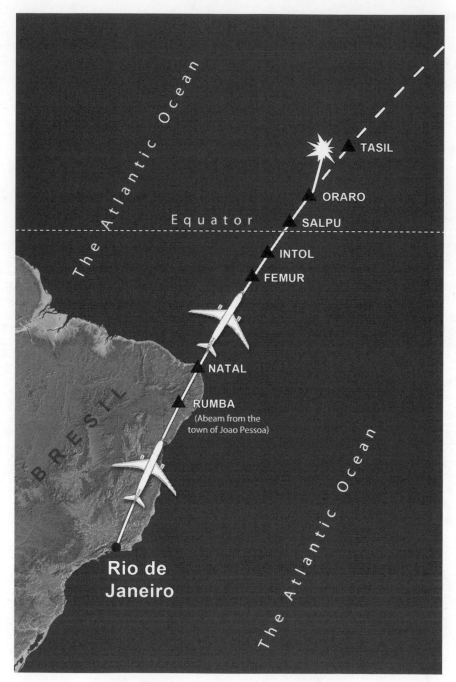

The route followed by the Airbus.

The INTER-TROPICAL CONVERGENCE ZONE (or INTER-TROPICAL FRONT)

The crash of Flight AF 447 cannot be dissociated from the weather conditions generally prevalent over the Atlantic at that time of the year. The Inter Tropical Front[17] is a belt of low pressure that undulates over the equator, the notorious doldrums so much dreaded by sailors. The enormous storm clouds that build up there each night have no equivalent under our latitudes. The ITF cumulonimbi can climb up to almost 50,000 feet[18]. No airliner can fly over them and it is impossible to fly through them because they have a core of powerful turbulence that would rip off the wings. There are also enormous hailstones which would shatter the windshields or destroy the engine blades. Entering an ITF cumulonimbus is a manoeuvre that can only end in disaster, whatever the aircraft.

In addition, these storm clouds are surrounded by zones of severe icing. To navigate through all these pitfalls, the cumulonimbus cloud masses have to be identified in advance by the weather radar and circumvented through a series of deviations. This takes time and flights are often delayed considerably but this is the only way safety can be guaranteed. To navigate in the ITF zone, the aircraft must have:

- Effective radar.
- An efficient de-icing system (especially for the Pitot tubes).

Photo of the ITCZ undulating along the line of the Equator (Photo: NASA).
This apparently harmless band of clouds is in reality an extremely dangerous meteorological phenomenon.

---

[17] Also known as the ITCZ – Inter Tropical Convergence Zone.
[18] A cumulonimbus rarely reaches 42,000 feet (11,000 m).

As if that was not enough, the ITF also causes problems in terms of the outside temperature. *It's hot out there*! At high altitudes, the temperature is a major parameter, playing a considerable role in an aircraft's flying performance – the hotter it is the higher an aircraft's stalling speed. So it is better to fly in cold air[19], especially when the aircraft is heavily-laden.

In order to dispose of a temperature reference, pilots use the "standard temperature", a sort of ideal temperature that ought to be prevalent in an atmosphere, in itself ideal. That is why the aircraft crew often used the term "Standard" to refer to too high an outside temperature. The ITF is a source of frequent upward warm air currents at altitude that can appear very suddenly and cause severe problems. Flying over Gabon, an airline pilot recently experienced the temperature rising in a few seconds to "standard + 40 degrees C". This brutal rise is often accompanied by violent turbulence. In this case, the pilot has no other option but to go down at once or risk seeing his aircraft leave its performance envelope resulting in stalling.

So, when going through the ITF, it is important to keep a close eye on the temperature to avoid any nasty surprises. This is precisely what Marc D did several times:

00:40:22 (Captain): *Plus 11… that's what they said, isn't it?*[20]

The temperature information was calculated by the aircraft's computer and clearly shown on the PFD screen. Here again this has nothing to do with what used to happen on an aircraft like the 737-200 where the pilots had to perform all sorts of complex calculations themselves with the help of data sheets and charts. All this is now of the past.

00:40:29 (First Officer right-hand seat): *What did you say to me?*

00:40:30 (Captain): *Standard plus 11. That's what they've planned…*

00:40:30 (First Officer right-hand seat): *Yeah…*

---

[19] The terms "cold" and "hot" must be understood to be relative since at level 350 the standard temperature is -55 degrees; so if the temperature is -45°, this is hot; if it is -57, this is cold. The standard temperature can be calculated rapidly using the following simple formula: T= 15 – flight level/10 x 2).

[20] Standard + 11 at level 350 means – 44 degrees.

The discussion continued. The crew realised that the computer forecast they would have 7.2 tons of fuel left when landing at Roissy-Charles de Gaulle. This was good news since the previous calculations had given 6.6 tons. The Airbus' fuel consumption was going to be lower than estimated. For a moment, the Captain and First Officer talked about the value of having good reserves of fuel in case of problems on arrival. If they had to pull up at Roissy or if the flaps jammed, the Captain did not want to have less than 6 tons. The more fuel they had, logically, the more they would feel reassured.

Since taking off from Rio, the weather conditions had been excellent and it appeared they were to stay that way since four minutes later the crew spotted the glow of city lights straight ahead of the aircraft.

00:44:45 (Captain): *That's Natal straight ahead.*

The coast then took a sharp turn to the left. Beyond, towards the north-east, everything was dark: this was the North Atlantic stretching out over more than 1,875 miles. On the other side lay Dakar and the African coast. According to the weather forecast, crossing the equator was going to be much as usual for that time of the year. The forecast stated that "the position of the ITF over the Atlantic was normal for the month of June. The piles of cumulonimbus in that zone were well and truly present all over the air space and going to last several hours."

In other words they would have to weave their way between storms. Apparently the idea of confronting this type of weather did not appear to worry the Captain since he added immediately:

00:44:49 (Captain): *We're not going to let a pile of cumulos bug us...*

Just as he said this the cockpit door opened and a hostess came in. She seemed to be worried by the temperature too although the concern was of a more trivial nature since she was talking about the temperature in the cargo compartment, where all the personal luggage was stored.

There followed a somewhat strange conversation:

00:46:07 (Hostess): *Er... what's the temperature in the hold?*

The First Officer glanced at his screen's ECAM[21] page and gave an immediate answer:

00:46:13 (First Officer right-hand seat): *Er... at the rear?*

00:46:13 (Hostess): *Where our luggage is!*

00:46:16 (First Officer right-hand seat): *At the moment it's 20 degrees there.*

Apparently it was too high for the hostess who asked him to lower the temperature in the hold; she had taken advantage of the trip to do some shopping and she was worried about the food she had bought being spoilt.

00:46:19 (Hostess): *Can you reduce it a bit. I've got some meat in my cases!*

00:46:19 (First Officer right-hand seat): *Oh. I ought to be able to. OK. There you are.*

00:46:19 (Hostess): *Sweet of you.*

00:46:31 (First Officer ironically): *We'll send you the fuel bill!*

The lights of Natal were now close. Outside, visibility was still excellent. In a few moments the Airbus would be flying over the "NTL" beacon and then leave land behind and head out over the Atlantic. The only lights visible from then on would be those of lightning flashes encountered as the ITF got nearer. For the crew, it was now the moment to check the weather forecast for the route one last time. For this, they contacted the Air France Operational Control Centre at Roissy. Even right in the middle of the Atlantic, the latest generation aircraft remain in contact with their airline. They do this by means of ACARS[22] messages. Like all Airbuses, the A330 is equipped with this communications system that enables a ground unit to talk to an aircraft located on the other side of the globe. Communications are by means of satellites or on the HF

---

[21] Electronic Centralised Aircraft Monitoring: the First Officer can obtain this information on the electronic screen that centralises most of the aircraft's parameters.

[22] Aircraft Communication Addressing System and Reporting System.

band[23] using a coded digital system. Two types of messages can therefore be exchanged:

- The crew can talk to the ground. These conversations are not carried out in the audio mode as with normal radio contact but go through a keyboard and a small thermal printer that unwinds rolls of paper on the central console of the aircraft. In Air France's case, these exchanges are mainly conducted with the Roissy Centre but the crew can also dialogue with other operators to obtain all sorts of information relating to meteorological, technical or medical issues. The latest systems can even be connected to the Internet. Some more laid back crews have even used the ACARS messages to book a table at a restaurant in the stopover or even to surf on the net[24]. ACARS messages also enable an aircraft that has lost touch with the ground to be re-contacted[25].

The messages arrive on a tiny thermal printer

---

[23] ACARS can also use the VHF band but the system then only has a limited range.

[24] See ERREURS de PILOTAGE 4, published by Altipresse.

[25] The controllers call them "Nordos" (No radio) and they are less rare than you may imagine. In this event, the controllers call the airline's dispatch by telephone and ask them to send an ACARS message to the silent aircraft. In this message there is a frequency on which the crew must contact the controller. In general the "mute" gets its power of speech back after a few minutes and everything returns to normal (See ERREURS de PILOTAGE 4).

- The aircraft's computer also uses ACARS messages to forward technical data to the airline's maintenance centre without intervention from the crew. Indeed, the aircraft sends off messages concerning any failures or anomalies it notes on board. The maintenance centre can therefore anticipate what repairs need to be carried out. When the aircraft arrives at the stand, the technicians are already there with the spare parts and the various circuit diagrams needed. Maintenance organization is thereby rationalised, making for considerable time saving. This system was to play an important role in a few hours' time when the Airbus faced its first difficulties. It was this system that signalled there was a speed indication problem.

The ACARS keyboard.
(photo Ken Wiens)

00:54:21 (Captain): *We'll be able to ask for the forecasts. For dispatch. I'm going to ask them to change the diversion airfields.*

00:54:26 (First Officer right-hand seat): *You asked for the forecasts, didn't you?*

00:54:29 (Captain): *No, no... Yeah, yeah, I did.*

00:54:32 (First Officer): *Oh Okay.*

To grasp the meaning of this exchange you have to be aware that the Airbus was making an ETOPS flight[26]. Being a twin-engined aircraft over the Atlantic, international regulations required it to be able to reach a diversion airport situated no more than 180 minutes flying time away in the event of engine failure. It was Air France Dispatch that decided on the diversion airports and the crew had just realised that one of the proposed fields was closed at night. It was the airport whose identification code was SID[27]. So they had to ask dispatch for an alternative one

00:54:37 (First Officer): *You doing the message or you want me to do it? Do you want me to do the first part or...?*

00:54:53 (Captain): *SID... What's that? Is that Natal?*

A pilot does not have to know the codes for all the world's airports by heart. However it did not take Pierre-Cedric B long to find the answer:

00:55:03 (First Officer): *SID. It's at Sal... Yes that's it. SID. It's Sal. You ask to change the back-up point clearly!*

00:56:50 (Captain): *Oh oh. It won't make much difference for us.*

The Captain began typing out a short ACARS message to ask the Air France Control Centre which airport they should use if they were forced to divert in the case of a problem. But just as he

---

[26] Extended Range OPerationS with two-engined aircraft.

[27] The three letters SID correspond to the IATA Code for the airport of Sal-Amilcar Cabral International on Cape Verde. The Cape Verde Islands are in the Atlantic 440 miles off the Senegal coast.

was sending the message he discovered that in the event of an emergency Sal airport could be opened at night.

00:57:41 (First Officer): *Ah shit... Well yes... It's allowed, they're right!*

As a result the tension dropped. There was no longer any need to make any special request to the OCC and all was well. It was even possible to think about taking a break.

00:58:07 (Captain): *Try and sleep perhaps for twenty minutes when he comes back or before if you want, ok?*

00:58:12 (First Officer): *Yeah, ok that's nice. For the moment I don't feel like it, but if I do, yeah.*

00:58:17 (Captain): *Yeah, it's going to be long for you.*

The First Officer kept the right-hand seat and even if no particular instruction was given to that effect, you can imagine that he was going to keep the controls when the Captain left for his rest. But one problem still had to be resolved. Twelve minutes earlier the crew had failed to understand a message from a controller who gave INTOL as the point where they were to change to HF with the "Atlantico" Centre. The aircraft was now moving on and they needed to resolve the matter.
The Captain examined his ND screen and tried to understand which point they were referring to. He seemed to hesitate: "Intol" or "Femur".

00:58:37 (Captain): *Where did they say to make the HF contacts, according to you? Was it at INTOL that it happens? It's not bad, at INTOL, Eh? FEMUR?*[28]

One cannot help but wonder why they did not just simply call the controller. No decision was made.
Four minutes later the flight deck door opened and the hostess entered again. The Captain seemed happy to see her:

01:03:43 (Captain): *We have a visitor!*

---

[28] The report points are positions situated on air routes; in general they don't correspond to any known geographical place. They always have five letters.

The newcomer explained that she still had a temperature problem but not in the hold this time but in the cabin. Some of the passengers were complaining.

01:03:53 (Hostess): *I'm at almost 25 degrees on my screen and they're still cold back there!*

There are two ways of changing the cabin temperature on an Airbus. Either a hostess can adjust it using a touch screen[29][28] located on partition L1 behind the cockpit or the pilots themselves can intervene from the flight deck. That evening it seemed the Cabin Senior Director was having trouble keeping the passengers warm at the back of the aircraft which is why she came to ask the Captain to handle the matter.

01:03:57 (First Officer): *Yeah, it's okay!*

01:04:01 (Captain joking): *It's okay we put a good shovelful of coal on it.*

Then remembering the hostess' problem with the meat she'd bought in Brazil, the First Officer added:

01:04:04 (First Officer): *In the rear hold it's now 7 degrees and it's going on down. That better?*

01:04:08 (Hostess): *In the hold... Ah, well. I was thinking of the... (incomprehensible)... for my meat.*

The conversation continued in a subdued manner. Firstly they talked about the meals served on board but then they moved on to technical aspects of the flight. The hostess asked questions to which the Captain replied patiently. He explained at length why aircraft like this Airbus 330 must have diversion airports when they cross the Atlantic.

---

[29] Apart from controlling the heating in the different cabin sections, this touch screen can be used to adjust the lighting, regulate the quantity of water in the toilets, check shutting of the doors and arming of the toboggans, be warned if a passenger is smoking in the toilets, activate the evacuation alarm and switch on the floor lighting to guide the passengers to the exits. From this panel, the Cabin Senior can even send information to the cockpit to tell them the cabin is ready for take-off or landing.

01:05:18 (Hostess): *I dunno why, because they've only got one engine, er... one engine not working very well.*

01:05:22 (Captain): *No, because normally there's the diversion field... the diversion field... You know for a twin engined aircraft, you have to have two diversion airports, there, when you cross the Atlantic... In the south, there's one that's closed from... hours...*

01:05:22 (Hostess): *So what?*

01:05:22 (Captain): *And they tell us they can open if we have to make an approach.*

01:05:22 (Hostess): *Ah. And then?*

01:05:22 (Captain): *So I asked them for another diversion field. It's not complicated...* (incomprehensible)...

The Captain explained his problem with the change of diversion airport at some length. He gave details about what had to be done in the event of engine failure and gave a description of Sal airport in the Cape Verde Islands. Once again he stated that the airport was closed but that in an emergency it could open again at night. There then followed an exchange between the Captain and the First Officer to decide whether it was a good idea for them to insist with the OCC and ask for a change of diversion airport. The First Officer appeared to be mildly critical of the Captain for his way of dealing with the problem.

01:10:35 (First Officer): *So. Er... His answer. We're happy with it, are we?*

01:10:36 (Captain): *What?*

01:10:39 (First Officer): *We're happy with his answer?*

01:10:41 (Captain): *Oh yes... I'm not really bothered very much, eh.*

01:10:47 (First Officer): *Yeah, well me neither... So, you going to ask him for a diversion point change?*

01:10:50 (Captain): *You don't sound worried?*

01:10:55 (First Officer): *It's a pity you didn't ask him for his opinion ...* (incomprehensible)*... to find another back-up point and if he answers: well, no it'll be like that, period.*

This time the reproach was barely veiled. In the First Officer's opinion, the Captain had lacked resolve in just accepting the OCC's decision to maintain Sal as the diversion airport without discussion. Far from seeking to assert himself the Captain was happy just to reply in a conciliatory tone:

01:11:05 (Captain): *It doesn't matter...*

This exchange is not anecdotal as it reveals the relationship that existed between the crew members. This is not Korean Air and the "Captain" seemed reluctant to impose his will in an authoritarian manner. Was it because he had handed over the controls of the aircraft? In all events the Captain made the right decision. After all, the Air France Operational Control Centre (OCC) confirmed that the airport at Sal could open at night in the event of a problem arising, why quibble about asking for another airport?

01:11:08 (First Officer): *OK. So we send him the things...*

01:11:12 (Captain): *Where is it... the answer? There... of the... Ah, you've entered it.*

01:11:19 (First Officer): *You'll be able to give it to David... you'll be able to tell him that...* (incomprehensible)*...*

During the whole of this conversation the hostess was present in the cockpit. Her words have not been re-transcribed here but she did come in from time to time on matters unrelated to the flight.

01:12:53 (Hostess): *Okay, well, I'm off.*

01:12:54 (Captain): *Okay. See you later.*

01:12:55 (Hostess): *See you later.*

The hostess left the cockpit but returned several times in the minutes that followed. The night flight remained calm with not a hint of turbulence. One minute later the aircraft overflew "Femur".

At that moment the Captain decided to contact Recife Control to give his position. Above all he wanted to ask whether he should contact the Atlantico Ocean Control Centre immediately.

01:14:30 (Captain): *Air France 447. We've checked "Femur" at 01 hour 13. Level 350... We contact "Atlantico" with the HF...*

This time the controller's answer was perfectly clear and there was no doubt that the Captain had made a mistake.

01:14:44 (Recife Controller): *Negative. After "Intol", call Atlantico on HF frequency on 6349.*

01:14:52 (Captain): *OK. Reporting "Intol"... Air France 447... Er... We keep this frequency with you.*

"Femur" was not the appropriate call point!

The minutes that followed were relatively peaceful. The aircraft kept heading 049 while the Captain and First Officer recovered weather information on the region with the various forecasts for the Atlantic. They made no comment on the storms they were going to encounter in the ITF. All seemed normal and there was not the slightest trace of anxiety in their conversation.
A quarter of an hour later, the Airbus approached the point where they had to change frequencies, but it was Recife control that called the aircraft first.

01:31:34 (Recife Controller): *Air France 447?*

01:31:40 (Captain addressing the First Officer): *We're coming up to "Intol".*

01:31:41 (Captain answering the Controller): *Air France 447. Go ahead.*

01:31:45 (Recife Controller): *Air France 447. Contact "Atlantico Centre" now on frequency 6619 5565... (incomprehensible)... frequency 6535...*

The message from Recife was somewhat garbled. Running figures all together like that with no pause for breath made the information confusing and there was a risk of misinterpretation. The Captain nevertheless managed in part to decipher what had been said:

01:32:01 (Captain): *I've understood: 6649 and 5565 and 6535.*

01:32:09 (Recife Controller): *It'll be 6535 only after TASIL with Dakar, Air France 447.*

01:32:16 (Captain): *OK. Bye-bye. Thanks.*

The controller seemed not to have noticed that the Captain made a mistake with the first Atlantico frequency (6649 and not 6619). Too late... the call was cut.

In the minutes following, various attempts to contact Dakar failed to get through. The Captain decided to call the airline on "Sel Call" to give his position: he estimated he would overfly "SALPU" at 01:18. Then it would be "ORARO" at 02:04. He would continue to maintain flight level 350.

Outside the weather was changing for the worse as they were now getting much closer to the ITF. They could feel the first turbulence. Nothing nasty but they were the first early warning signs of the storms to come and the sky was gradually getting darker. From time to time, the aircraft broke into zones where the temperature was higher:

01:36:44 (Captain): *Standard + 12.*

This high outside temperature obviously raised the problem mentioned earlier. The aircraft would never be able to fly over the bad weather as it was still too heavy. This would only be possible once it had used up more of its fuel and become lighter. The First Officer clearly understood this:

01:36:47 (First Officer): *Yes... yes... always otherwise we'll be able to catch a higher level...*

01:36:48 (Captain): *Ah yes... climb slightly later...* (incomprehensible)... *340.*

01:36:50 (First Officer): *Yeah.*

The Airbus was now flying along level with a layer of cloud, occasionally making brief incursions into it. The turbulence then became more persistent. Tiny little white filaments sometimes flew past on either side of the windshield. They were characteristic of what was going on outside:

01:37:03 (Captain): *It's snowing!*

In answer the First Officer gave the indicated airspeed of the aircraft

01:37:04 (First Officer): *209 knots[30].*

The situation of Flight 447 at that time can be summarised as follows: The Airbus had just reached the ITF and the weather was beginning to deteriorate. The clouds coming up in front of the aircraft were cumulonimbi and for the moment, with the outside temperature being too high, it was impossible for the aircraft to overfly them. The aircraft would have to get lighter by using up some of its fuel but that would take too long. The computer told them that all the conditions for the aircraft to be able to climb to level 370 safely would only be met in four hours. If the pilot attempted to climb now, he would risk stalling the aircraft. The only way to advance safely through the ITF was therefore to make changes in heading so as to avoid the zones shown by the radar in "red".
Strangely enough, for the time being there were none.
Remember there was nothing unusual about this weather situation in that particular region. Hundreds of aircraft passed through the zone every day successfully making the necessary deviations.
The two crewmen were still relaxed as their conversation for the next five minutes turned to "tax havens". The atmosphere was peaceful. Other commercial traffic could be heard in the loudspeakers communicating with "Atlantico" control.
The discussion about tax havens only came to an end when the First Officer started concentrating on the radar screen of his Navigation Display. As there were still no storm cells in sight in front of the aircraft, he modified the detection scale, reducing it from 320 to 160 nautical miles[31].

---

[30] 242 mph. This speed is related to the air. This bears no relation to the ground speed or the Airbus's Mach number.
[31] The scale went from 375 miles to 187.5 miles.

01:42:15 (First Officer): *There's something straight ahead... there's another one behind it...*

The First Officer had just made out a massed formation of clouds that seemed threatening but he appeared to consider them sufficiently remote since there was no mention of evasive action and the discussion on tax havens continued.
A few moments later the First Officer abruptly changed topics. His words were incomprehensible but must have been portentous as the Captain reacted fiercely:

01:44:42 (Captain): *What, Ah shit, no!*

It is quite likely that at this moment the aircraft was about to enter the cloud layer. For the moment, there was nothing to show they were approaching a cumulonimbus. The First Officer however cautiously took an initiative so as better to evaluate the situation better.

01:46:14 (First Officer): *I'm lowering the lights just to see better outside.*

01:46:15 (Captain): *Yes, yes.*

01:46:19 (First Officer): *I'm putting the headlights on, just to see...*

The cockpit was now plunged in semi-darkness as though they were doing a night landing. Only six screens lit up the place. Outside the headlights tore through the darkness. The cloud layer was close under the aircraft and the beams intermittently reflected off the whitish mass.

01:46:20 (First Officer): *Ah yes, indeed.*

01:46:21 (Captain): *What?*

01:46:23 (First Officer): *I think we're going to enter the cloud.*

Once again however, there was nothing dramatic and nobody seemed to be unduly worried. Not even the hostess who was about to leave the flight deck.

01:46:30 (Hostess): *I'm the one who's looking after things… David's going to…* (incomprehensible)*… I'm going to eat.*

As she left, the Captain could not help but show his consideration…

01:46:34 (Captain): *Yes, my… my honey.*

Clearly Flight 447 was not the only one to be running into bad weather. At the same time, the other Air France aircraft 190 miles behind it was faced with a similar problem. This was Flight 459, the one that had been the cause of the mix-up earlier. Its crew called "Atlantico" to ask for a deviation.
Their conversation was heard by Flight 447.

01:50:11 (Flight AF 459): *Air France 459?*

01:50:18 (Atlantico): *Air France 459. Go ahead.*

01:50:21 (AF 459): *Air France 459. We're deviating 15 degrees on the right to avoid some "Charlie Bravos"[32].*

01:50:33 (Atlantico): *OK. Air France 459. Call when you're back on your route.*

01:50:37 (AF 459): *We'll call when back on our route in about … er… 100 nautical miles[33].*

Three weeks after the tragedy, the Captain of Flight 459 explained to newspapers that that night he had succeeded in detecting the cumulonimbus by tuning his weather radar in a special way. "It's something that Flight 447 might not have done."…"It's sure not everybody does this manoeuvre[34]."
The conversation between Flight 459 and the Atlantico controller was also heard in the Airbus cockpit. The crew however was exploring the possibility of going up to level 370 and appeared not to have heard the dialogue. It was also logical that what was going on behind them was of little concern to them. The two men therefore made no comment.

---

[32] Cumulonimbi.

[33] 115.6 miles.

[34] In Le Figaro, 24 June 2009.

After some reflection, the First Officer suggested going up to level 360. It was cutting it a bit fine for the aircraft's weight but according to him, it ought to get through.

The Captain hesitated, then finally answered:

01:50:32 (Captain): *We'll wait a bit...*

Interference due to the electrical disturbance caused by the storms started echoing over the radio frequencies during the discussion. This phenomenon seemed to surprise the crew as there was no lightning. The Captain of Flight 459 confirmed later that night that the storms were not causing any great electrical activity and so very little lightning. This was rather rare when going through the ITF... However, Flight AF 447 was subjected to new, very spectacular electrical phenomena.

01:51:10 (Captain): *Ah well, that's all we needed!*

The First Officer had difficulty hiding his surprise. It was no doubt the first time he had encountered manifestations of this type.

01:51:14 (First Officer): *Ah...* (incomprehensible)... *or what there?*

01:51:21 (Captain): *That's all that was missing: Mr Saint-Elmo.*

The Airbus was indeed being subjected to a phenomenon called Saint Elmo's Fire. Violet glows appeared on certain parts of the airframe, generally on the windshield, on the wings and the wing tips[35]. These strange sparks are always produced in stormy regions and in particular when an aircraft is flying over a cumulonimbus[36]. Once again the First Officer was surprised.

01:51:30 (First Officer): *... didn't think there was any storm.*

---

[35] The reader can find a lot of examples of videos on Youtube showing St-Elmo's fire in the cockpits. Here's one example among others: http://www.youtube.com/watch?v=Py5mkrrcLPU&NR=1

[36] The phenomenon appears on the top of the masts of sailing boats and used to frighten sailors as it often preceded a lightning strike.

This remark confirmed once again what the crew of Flight AF459 declared later. "That night, the storm mass was difficult to detect visually because there wasn't any lightning." Remember however that such electrical storms were not exceptional; this was the equator and they were normal weather conditions for the time of year. Caution was required but even if the Airbus was struck by

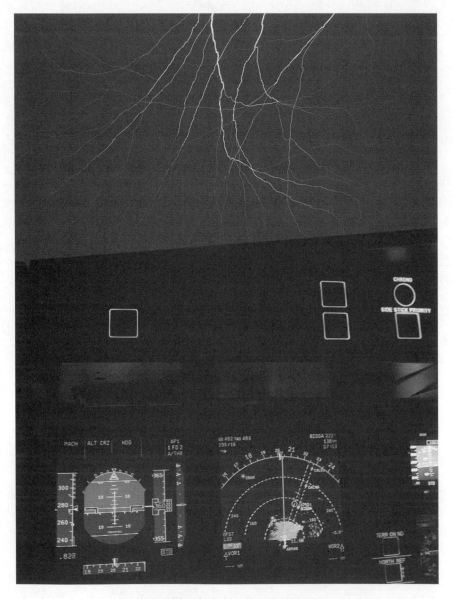

Saint Elmo's fire on a windshield.

lightning there would be no harmful effect, except perhaps the passengers being scared by the phenomenon. An aircraft behaves like a Faraday's cage and is perfectly well protected against violent electrical discharges[37].

At the same moment, the turbulence started again but it was moderate and the Captain showed no signs of worry:

01:51:58 (Captain): *It's going to be turbulent when I go off for my nap.*

For a few moments, the crew talked about the REC/MAX, the maximum level that they could reach. Once again the Captain decided that the temperature was too high and they would have to wait. Then, four minutes later, he decided it was time for him to leave the cockpit.

01:55:57 (Captain): *Good... well... better go and wake him up, then, eh?*

The person to be woken up was obviously David R who was to replace him. At that moment the cockpit was still in semi-darkness and the Captain was getting ready to leave his seat.

01:56:00 (Captain): *Want me to put the lights up a bit?*

01:56:01 (First Officer): *Yeah.*

He pushed the Flight Rest button to send a sound signal to the second First Officer who apparently was not sleeping deeply since he replied at once by tapping on the partition to tell them he was coming in.
There were still two problems to be settled:
- Where would the newcomer sit?
- Who was going to be in charge when the Captain left the flight deck, since there were only two First Officers and one had to be designated to replace the Captain?

---

[37] A Faraday cage is a metallic box insulated from electrical fields. An aircraft behaves just like a car insulated from the ground by its tyres and its occupants have nothing to fear from storms as long as there is no earthing braid designed to get rid of static.

01:56:16 (Captain): *Er... who's landing this thing...you? Good ok, he'll take my seat...*

The reasoning was simple. Since it was the right-hand pilot who would land the aircraft at Roissy he was the one to remain PF. When the Captain talked about taking his seat, he certainly meant the left-hand seat[38]. This did not mean that David R replaced him. It was even exactly the opposite since he then asked immediately:

01:56:20 (Captain): *You're an ATPL, aren't you?*

01:56:21 (First Officer right-hand seat): *Yeah.*

From a regulation point of view, the question Marc D had just asked was important. Before letting Pierre-Cedric B take his place as replacement pilot he had to check that he was indeed the holder of an ATP licence. This was essential as a CPL[39] was not adequate. Now although they addressed each other in the second person singular ("tu") they did not know each other. Note that this point could have been brought up beforehand during the pre-flight briefing but was not. As the First Officer confirmed that he did have the required licence, he could replace the Captain[40]. As soon as the Captain left the flight deck the First Officer would be wearing two hats: he would be at the controls of the Airbus, and he would be in authority. This was a big responsibility when you are at the controls of an aircraft carrying 216 passengers.
It was at this moment that the second First Officer entered the cockpit. The Captain pushed his seat back to let him take the left hand seat.

01:59:32 (Captain): *Good, okay,*

01:59:38 (First Officer Pierre-Cédric B): *Sleep well?*

01:59:40 (First Officer David R): *So-so.*

01:59:44 (Captain): *Didn't you sleep?*

---

[38] Translator's note: the French word "place" means both "position" and "ranking", as well as "seat". Hence the possible confusion.

[39] Commercial Pilot's Licence.

[40] The regulations allow the Captain to hand over flight control to another pilot on condition that the aircraft is above 20,000 feet.

01:59:47 (First Officer Pierre-Cédric B): *He says: So-so, so-so, so-so.*

David R sat down in the Captain's seat and the Captain decided there wasn't anything left for him to do.

02:00:08 (Captain): *Right, I'm off.*

However, he did not leave immediately but stayed on a moment to take part in the briefing that Pierre-Cédric gave for the benefit of the newcomer and bring him up to date as to the situation.

02:00:19 (First Officer David R): *I... I snoozed in fact. You ok?*

02:00:33 (First Officer Pierre-Cédric B): *I'm OK. Right, the little bit of turbulence that you've just felt, there should be the same ahead. In fact we're inside the layer...Unfortunately we can't go higher for the moment because the temperature is going down slower than forecast!*

02:00:44 (First Officer David R): *Yeah.*

02:00:45 (First Officer Pierre-Cédric B): *So that gives us REC/ MAXs which are a little bit low to climb to level 370. It's a real pity.*

The First Officer's briefing was clear. The REC MAX is the maximum flight level recommended for flight safely. For an aircraft with an equivalent weight, this depends mainly on the outside temperature. And that night, as has already been seen, the temperature was not what had been announced in the weather forecasts. The Airbus therefore had to fly into the cloud layer and as a result it was most likely going to run into more sustained turbulence.
Pierre-Cédric carried on with his briefing about the radio communications situation.

02:00:52 (First Officer Pierre-Cédric): *Otherwise we're in HF contact with Atlantico.*

02:01:02 (First Officer David): *Hmm, Hmm...*

02:01:20 (First Officer David): *The log-on failed with Dakar[41]. Of course we're in contact with dispatch[42].*

Then addressing the Captain, who was still standing behind them:

02:01:22 (First Officer): *Can you remind me what exactly the frequencies they gave us were, please?*

Once again you might be surprised by the unusual tone the First Officer used with the Captain. All the more so as Marc D was not expecting the question.

02:01:29 (Captain): *Eh?*

02:01:30 (First Officer Pierre-Cédric): *The frequencies? Which one's which?*

02:01:31 (Captain): *Er... 6649. 5565 then after it's 6535.*

The other First Officer understood since he confirmed immediately:

02:01:39 (First Officer David R.): *From "TASIL", onwards it's 6535!*

This time the Captain left. The cockpit Voice Recorder recorded a clack resembling the sound of the door lock closing.
The two First Officers were left alone in the cockpit...
So, to again recap the emerging situation:
- The Airbus was in the Inter Tropical Front and it appeared there were several cumulonimbi on its route. The appearance of Saint-Elmo's Fire suggested they had just flown over one... Because of the high temperature, the aircraft could not fly any higher and no change in heading had been considered by the crew.
- The Captain had left the flight deck to sleep in the couchette.
- Sitting in the left-hand seat was David R who had just entered the cockpit after his rest period. We understand that he was going to handle radio communications.

---

[41] The log-on ADS-C is a system that enables the aircraft's equipment to transmit navigation and position information to the control (there's no radar coverage of the South Atlantic). The installations are located at Cayenne-Rochambeau in French Guyana.
[42] The Air France Operational Control Centre.

- Sitting in the right-hand seat was Pierre-Cédric B. He was the less experienced of the two First Officers but by asking him if he had an airline pilot's licence, the Captain inferred that he was entrusting him with the task of replacing him. He was therefore the boss!

In fact, the respective tasks had not been clearly assigned. The uncertainty as to the real responsibilities almost certainly played a role in subsequent events.

The information displayed on the screen of the Primary Flight Display was perfectly normal:

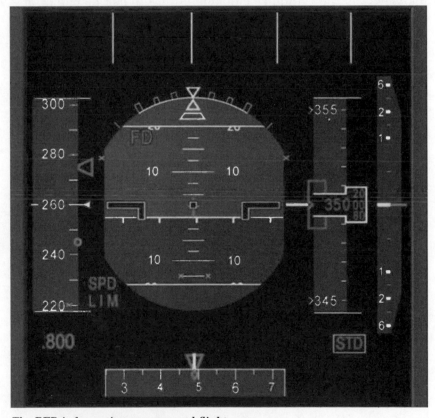

The PFD information on a normal flight.
Indicated AirSpeed was 260 knots (left-hand scale)
The aircraft was flying at Mach 0.8 (.800)
The attitude was 2.5 degrees (Artificial horizon)
The flight level was 350 (first graduated scale on the right)
The variometer was at zero (scale on the right)
The heading was 049 (scale at the bottom of the screen)

For a few minutes, the two First Officers talked about the HF frequencies that could be used on the route. Then Pierre-Cédric B explained what he would do if he only had one engine:

02:02:32 (First Officer Pierre-Cédric B): *For the moment if we had a problem, we'd turn around and head back to Natal where the weather's fine...*

02:02:37 (First Officer David R): *Agreed.*

Pierre-Cédric B took advantage of his absence to criticise what in his view was the Captain's culpable failure to ask dispatch for a change of diversion field.

02:02:47 (First Officer Pierre-Cédric B): *Ah. Well actually, Marc, he sent a message asking, asking for a change of diversion point... He didn't ask, er, yes, he said that he was requesting a diversion change "Wotsit".*

This was not very clear but one is left with the impression that the First Officer would have acted differently.
While the two men were talking, the Airbus was flying at Mach 0.82 and heading for bad weather. Light turbulence could be felt once again, nothing too uncomfortable but the aircraft was probably approaching the head of another cumulonimbus[43].
Pierre-Cédric B pointed at the zone in question on his ND.

02:03:44 (First Officer Pierre-Cédric): *The inter tropical convergence, there we are, right in it. Between "SALPU" and "TASIL"... and then, there you are, we're right in it...*

As the turbulence became stronger, David R noted that the temperature was higher than forecast. It was "standard + 10", which still prevented them from climbing. He suggested warning the hostesses for them to take the usual precautions because there was a risk of the buffeting getting worse.

---

[43] As the ITF gets closer, this turbulence is nearly always accompanied by a sudden rise in temperature, which can obviously lead to a problem of lift. In the present instance, however, contrary to what the weather forecast had predicted, the temperature did not drop.

02:05:55 (First Officer David R): *Yeah, I'll call them, back there. To tell them all the same...*

David therefore pressed on the chimes and the answer was almost immediate:

02:05:59 (Hostess): *Yes? Marylin.*

But it was Pierre-Cédric B who addressed her.

02:06:04 (First Officer Pierre-Cédric): *Yes. Marylin. It's Pierre up front... Listen in a few moments we're going into a zone where it's going to move about a bit more than now, better watch out, now.*

02:06:13 (Hostess): *Ok, do we sit?*

02:06:15 (First Officer Pierre-Cédric): *Well, yes I think it'd be a good idea. Tell the others okay!*

02:06:18 (Hostess): *Yeah. Okay. I'll tell the others back there. Thanks a lot.*

Then to reassure the young woman, the First Officer added:

02:06:19 (First Officer Pierre-Cédric B): *But I'll tell you just as soon as we're out of it again.*

02:06:20 (Hostess): *Okay.*

Several seconds went by then David R once again examined the temperature on his screen and was unable to hide his surprise. It had just gone up rapidly.

02:06:40 (First Officer David R): *Standard + 13! Bloody hell. Thank God we're in a 330, eh? We wouldn't be such wise guys in a full 340[44]!*

02:06:45 (First Officer Pierre-Cédric R): *Dead right!*

---

[44] An allusion to the difference in performance between the Airbus 330 and the Airbus 340.

Having discussed the relative merits of Airbus aircraft in this light-hearted vein, the First Officers had a good laugh. Clearly, the abrupt rise in temperature did not worry them.
Then Pierre-Cédric in turn looked at the temperature.

02:06:50 (First Officer Pierre-Cédric): *Minus 42 C... Okay... Let's put the de-icers on. That'll be that done at least.*

As already said, -42 was warm at that altitude. As David R had just said, this meant a temperature of "standard +13 degrees". Ironically, the de-icing system had to be switched on because the aircraft was not flying in clear sky but inside the cloud layer. Ice could therefore contaminate sensitive points of the airframe. This phenomenon had to be prevented.

02:07:00 (First Officer Pierre-Cédric B): *Apparently we're on the edge of the layer... it should be all right.*

David R however seemed less optimistic than his colleague. Examining the weather radar on his ND screen attentively, he noted that the system had not been configured so as best to detect thunderstorm cells. The radar was set to the "calibrated" mode. He corrected this by setting it to the "maximum gain" position and realised at that instant that the conditions were certainly *not* as good as they thought. There were heavy rumbling echoes coming from the sky ahead of them although he had the impression the storms were developing a little less to the left.
So he made a suggestion to the man in charge.

2:08:03 (First Officer David R): *You can pull it a bit to the left if you want.*

2:08:06 (First Officer Pierre-Cédric B): *Sorry?*

02:08:07 (First Officer David R): *You can take it a bit to the left if you want. I agree we're on manual, aren't we?*

David R had just suggested altering the heading so as to avoid the bad weather. Pierre-Cédric said nothing but reduced the heading by 12 degrees to the left. The heading was now 037. Then suddenly he not help gut shout out. A strong, pungent smell had invaded the flight deck. It resembled the smell to be found near electrical transformers and suddenly it became hotter:

02:08:36 (First Officer Pierre-Cédric B): *Oh God! Have you touched the air conditioning?*

02:08:39 (First Officer David R): *I haven't touched anything!*

02:08:41 (First Officer Pierre-Cédric B): *No, the air conditioning? What's that smell?*

The phenomenon did not appear to faze David R... With more experience than his colleague, he had immediately understood what was happening and did not see any reason for concern.

02:08:43 (First Officer David R): *It's ozone... it's ozone...*[45]

02:08:45 (First Officer Pierre-Cédric B): *It's ozone, is that it? Are we agreed?*

02:08:47 (First Officer David R): *It's ozone, that's why...*

02:08:48 (First Officer Pierre-Cédric B): *Already. You can feel it's much hotter.*

02:08:50 (First Officer David R): *That's why it's hotter and ozonic!*

02:09:01 (First Officer Pierre-Cédric B): *What's that? Something to do with the ITF?*

02:09:07 (First Officer David R): *Ozone? It's air charged with electricity.*

02:09:10 (First Officer Pierre-Cédric B): *No? Ah yes, okay...*

This was clearly the first time Pierre-Cédric had encountered this sort of phenomenon. The smell of ozone appearing at high altitude often indicates the presence of electrically active rapidly developing cumulonimbus.

The seconds passed, a little tensely. Pierre-Cédric seemed ill at ease:

---

[45] Ozone (or tri-oxygen 03) is formed by the action of the electric field caused by storms on oxygen. It has a characteristic smell that can be encountered near transformers or certain electrical machines when in operation. Although it is highly toxic in large quantities, it is ozone that gives the sky its beautiful blue colour.

02:09:20 (First Officer Pierre-Cédric B): *It's surprising how hot it is all of a sudden.*

Then suddenly, the background noise changed considerably in the cockpit. The investigators think that this was the result of ice crystals appearing on certain parts of the airframe. The aerodynamic flow would have been almost imperceptibly changed. As Pierre-Cédric B did not react, David R took the initiative of reducing the Mach speed to 0.80. It is never a good idea to be flying too fast when things start taking a turn for the worse.

02:09:54 (First Officer David R): *There we are, I've reduced a bit, there...*

02:10:00 (First Officer Pierre-Cédric B): *Doesn't cost anything!*

02:10:02 (First Officer David R): *Go on!*

02:10:03 (First Officer Pierre-Cédric B): *Do you want us to put it on "Ignition Start"?*[46]

At this stage the tasks seem to have been shared out somewhat haphazardly between the PF and PNF. As their roles had not been clearly defined when the Captain left the flight deck, they did not know who was to decide on what. Incongruously, it was Pierre-Cédric who had just asked whether he should switch on the ignition start of the engines.

The FATEFUL FOUR MINUTES

Suddenly the "Cavalry Charge" alarm sounded. It lasted just 2.2 seconds to signal that the autopilot had just disconnected. Pierre-Cédric grabbed the mini-stick on his right and announced:

02:10:06.4 (First Officer Pierre-Cédric B): *I've got the controls.*

02:10:07.5 (First Officer David R): *All right.*

---

[46] In the case of heavy icing, Ignition Start prevents the engines being extinguished. It keeps the flame burning in the combustion chamber so that, should pieces of ice be ingested by the air intakes, they will not stifle the engine.

It was probably at this moment that the Pitot tubes iced over. This icing incident has never been fully explained. Was the anti-icing switched on too late? Was the phenomenon particularly strong that night? Was it a defect in the Pitot tube heating system? Whatever it was, the probes got blocked by ice and no longer provided airspeed information. The indication disappeared off the PFD. The computer instantly switched over to "Alternate" law. Certain computerised protective systems were no longer activated and the auto-throttles were blocked in the position they were in. This meant that the computer no longer stabilised the power in relation to the aircraft's needs: it was now up to the First Officers themselves to adjust the thrust of the engines.

With the autopilot disconnected, the effect of turbulence was no longer countered and the Airbus banked slightly 8.4° to the right. The situation was still far from dramatic. After the accident, many pilots tested the situation in an Airbus 330 simulator and the aircraft never took on a position representing the slightest danger. It remained perfectly stable[47].

At that moment, all that was needed was for the First Officer to move his mini-stick very slightly to the left and bring the wings back to the horizontal and the incident would have had no dire consequences. This was basic flying and presented no difficulty for a well trained crewman.

Unfortunately, this was not what happened... As Pierre-Cédric B took hold of the stick, his reaction was quite out of proportion. With something of a panic reflex, he positioned the stick on "pull up" or ¾ of its maximum position and held this. The pitch attitude of the Airbus climbed to 11 degrees and the aircraft started climbing with a vertical speed of 5,200 feet per minute.

At that altitude, such a climb rate was enormous.

Obviously a second alarm sounded at once. This was the "C-Chord" that warns the pilots the aircraft has quit the altitude for which it was programmed. It was no longer at level 350!

They had to descend...

Finally, the stall alarm resounded (as is normal given the fact that speed was decreasing rapidly and above all the angle of attack had increased brutally to 5 degrees[48]).

---

[47] The author has personally tested the situation in an A 330 simulator and has come to the same conclusions. The aircraft does not budge.

[48] The alarm is triggered when the angle of incidence exceeds 4 degrees.

The stall alarm is a synthetic voice warning expressed in a deep male voice:

02:10:10.4 (Synthetic voice): *STALL!*

The word "Stall" is followed by a strange sound called a "Cricket", a kind of ringing noise that is deliberately unpleasant so as not to go unnoticed. The "stall" warning has priority over all the other alarms in the cockpit. These are reduced to silence for nothing can be more serious than stalling. Stalling at high altitude is the worst thing that can happen to an aircraft.

02:10:11 (Synthetic voice): *STALL!*

02:10:11.3 (First Officer David R): *What's that?*

When the stall alarm sounds in an aircraft, the immediate reaction of any well trained pilot is to push. At flying schools, the trainees are taught that if they hear this alarm, it means that the aircraft's nose is too far up and the angle of attack is too high. The only way to recover is to push the stick to "dive", i.e. forward as a matter of utmost urgency!
Now, the First Officer did exactly the opposite. He pulled up... This is an instinctive reaction encountered in many trainee pilots during their early stall training.
It would be to no purpose here to recount all the figures relating to the angle of attack, the pitch attitude and the aircraft's speed as shown by the flight recorders. Suffice it to say that throughout these events, Pierre-Cédric B's use of the joystick was always brutally exaggerated as he continued to "pull up".
So the Stall alarm was maintained:

02:10:13 (Synthetic voice): *STALL!*

02:10:13.4 (Synthetic voice): *STALL!*

02:10:15.1 (First Officer Pierre-Cédric B): *We don't have a good... we don't have a good indication... of speed.*

02:10:15.9 (First Officer David R): *We've lost the speed, have we?*

The Airbus continued to climb. Three seconds later, its vertical speed was increasing by 6,700 feet per minute. It is hard to imagine an airliner reaching such a rate of climb at that altitude. And the laws of physics are incontrovertible. An aircraft weighing more than 200 tons cannot just keep shooting up towards the stratosphere indefinitely: the airspeed dropped to 93 knots and the Mach to 0.29... Note in passing that the aircraft proved compliant since the pilot also rolled it brutally. The Airbus banked from one wing to the other. In identical circumstances many other aircraft would have responded much more drastically and most of them would certainly have stalled. We have seen earlier how a Tupolev 154 went into a flat spin for much less than this...

Now the Airbus just banked peacefully ten or so degrees to the right and left without abruptly dropping off into the void. The problem was that each time it banked, the First Officer again reacted disproportionately by pulling the stick as far as it would go. Since the very start of these problems, the way he reacted on the controls had been quite out of proportion to what was actually happening. His movements were completely excessive.

It was the second First Officer who first realised that the parameters were deteriorating very seriously: the rate of climb was now 7,000 feet per minute!

02:10:27 (First Officer David R): *Watch your speed!*

02:10:28.3 (First Officer David R): *Watch your speed!*

02:10:28.3 (First Officer Pierre-Cédric B): *Okay. Okay. I'm going down.*

02:10:30 (First Officer David R): *You're stabilising...*

02:10:30.7 (First Officer Pierre-Cédric B): *Yeah...*

02:10:31.2 (First Officer David R): *Go down... We're going up according to that. According to that you're going up. So, go down!*

02:10:35.2 (First Officer Pierre-Cédric B): *Okay.*

It is important to note that the Pitot tubes had been iced over for 29 seconds now. With the action of the de-icing system however, probe No 1 had just started functioning again. The airspeed showed up at once on the left PFD. The information was coherent again but the crew apparently failed to notice that the problem had partially been resolved. On the right, Pierre-Cédric continued to shake the machine excessively. The Airbus was now at 37,124 feet.

Clearly very worried now, David R insisted:

02:10:36.4 (First Officer David R): *Go down!*

02:10:36.7 (First Officer Pierre-Cédric B): *We're off, we're going down.*

Then because obviously, once again, his action was excessive, David R warned:

02:10:38.5 (First Officer David R): *Gently!*

David R was right. They had to reduce their attitude and return to the initial cruising level. Pierre-Cédric let off pulling on his mini-stick and the airspeed rose quickly from 105 to 223 knots. As for the vertical speed, it dropped to 1,100 feet per minute, still too much for this altitude but a slightly more reasonable figure. All the Airbus wanted to do was carry on flying level and to let it do so all they had to do was refrain from pulling back on the stick. The roll seemed to be under control too. The angle of attack went below 5 degrees. The stall alarm fell silent... The situation would improve if Pierre-Cédric would just let off a bit with his stick. He needed to dive gently and above all resist the instinctive temptation of all beginners who want to hold the aircraft back when it is going to stall. The BEA investigators explained later that at that moment the flight path of the Airbus could have been mastered...

02:10:41.6 (First Officer Pierre-Cédric B): *We're on... yeah... we're on "climb"...*

In the left-hand seat, David R seemed to understand that his colleague was not going to succeed in recovering the situation. The Captain had to come back. Whilst pressing the call button that chimed in the couchettes next door, he cried out:

02:10:49.8 (First Officer David R): *Shit, where is he? ... Er?*

At that moment, the Airbus was at 37,512 feet. This was more than 2,500 feet above its initial cruising level. However, at no moment did the right-hand stick go into the "dive" position. What was worse… after being in the neutral position, it gradually slipped backwards. The result was immediate: in spite of the engine thrust, the angle of attack increased immediately, reaching 13 degrees, and the stall alarm's powerful voice resounded again:

02:10:51.2 (Synthetic voice): *STALL!* [49]

02:10:51.4 (Synthetic voice): *STALL!*

02:10:53 (Synthetic voice): *STALL!*

02:10:54.2 (Synthetic voice): *STALL!*

On the right, there was no reaction… Not a word. Strangely, only David R seemed to realise that something abnormal was going on. He exploded:

02:10:54.9 (First Officer David R): *Fucking hell!*

At the same moment someone called on the interphone, but not the Captain.

02:10:55.9 (woman's voice): *Hello?*

02:10:56.8 (Synthetic voice): *STALL!*

02:10:57.6 (Synthetic voice): *STALL!*

This was the ninth time the stall alarm had sounded since the beginning of the problem and strangely enough the crew still seemed to be ignoring it. It was now 54 seconds since the anemometric probes had iced over. We have seen that probe N° 1 had started working again after a 29 second interruption. Now probe N° 3 was working again and the data it sent was coherent. The CAS ISIS speed showed up again on the right hand screen and there should

---

[49] Despite the repetitive nature of these stall alarm calls, they are all transcribed here with the exact time they were set off. Indeed they were vitally important in the succession of events and cannot be ignored.

have been no further problem[50]. All that remained was for the effects of the right-hand First Officer's compulsive movements to be brought under control:

02:10:59.4 (woman's voice on the interphone): *Yes?*

Let us devote a few words now to explain what happens during a stall. On most aircraft, when the angle of attack reaches a limit, there is no longer enough lift and the aircraft stalls. In general, the nose drops brutally. We say it is "saluting"[51]. As already stated, it is often at this moment that trainees react badly by pulling the stick backward to try and neutralise the fall. The correct reaction is to do precisely the opposite: when the aircraft stalls or when it is on the point of doing so, the pilot should follow up the "salute" by pushing forward on the stick. Thus as the attitude diminishes, the angle of attack returns to its normal level and lift is recovered.

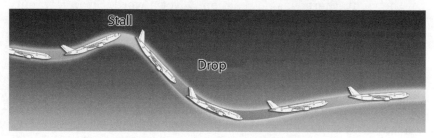

Recovery of a classic stall after a drop

Now in the present instance, the First Officer had been making almost non-stop "pull up" movements for a minute now. Every time the aircraft gathered a bit of airspeed, he blocked it at once. The Airbus was behaving rather like a horse you wanted to gallop while pulling back strongly on the reins. Under such conditions the aircraft does not "salute" but remains with its nose in the air and the situation can only deteriorate.

Obviously at a loss what to do, the First Officer decided to set full power on both engines and pushed both levers full forward. Each engine was now giving almost 35 tons of thrust! Surprising as it may seem, despite the conditions, the airplane's altitude increased again, going up from 37,512 to 37,596 feet!

---

[50] Probe N° 2 is on the left-hand side but its parameters are not recorded (the regulations do not require this). So it is not known at what moment it started functioning again.

[51] The technical term is "drop".

02:11:00 (Synthetic voice): *STALL!*

Remember that right from the start of events Pierre-Cédric B was the one moving his joystick. At no time did David R take over the controls. However, the way his colleague was shaking up the aircraft clearly annoyed him and he would certainly not have been so brutal in his reactions.

02:11:00.2 (First Officer David R): *Above all try to move the ailerons as little as possible, eh!*

This latest remark suggests that David R was beginning to understand what was really going on. It is indeed important to deflect the ailerons as little as possible during a stall.

02:11:01.2 (Synthetic voice): *STALL!*

02:11:02.6 (Synthetic voice): *STALL!*

The woman's voice resounded again in the speakers. There is nothing to say whether it was the hostess who was worried about the aircraft's movements or someone answering the call from the cockpit.

02:11:02.3 (woman's voice on the interphone): *Hello?*

02:11:03.1 (First Officer Pierre-Cédric B): *I'm on TOGA, aren't I?*[52]

The engines were delivering full power and Pierre-Cédric seemed surprised not to see the aircraft setting off again. There was unfortunately no chance of the aircraft recovering because he was still pulling the joystick back. The Airbus was certainly powerful but it wasn't a Mirage 2000 capable of climbing vertically!

02:11:03.1 (Synthetic voice): *STALL!*

02:11:05.3 (Synthetic voice): *STALL!*

02:11:05.9 (Synthetic voice): *STALL!*

---

[52] Take Off Go Around: maximum thrust used for taking off and pulling up.

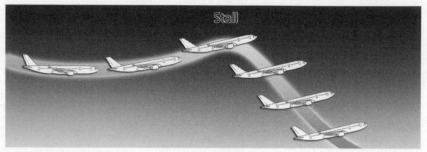

The Airbus stalling.
The attitude remains nose-up and there is no reduction in the angle of attack.

Suddenly, David R became angry as things were clearly deteriorating. He had called the Captain more than a minute ago and he had still not come back to the cockpit. They obviously needed him.

02:11:06.3 (First Officer David R): *Fucking hell! Is he coming or not?*

02:11:08.8 (Synthetic voice): *STALL!*

02:11:09.6 (Synthetic voice): *STALL!*

It was at this precise moment that the Airbus reached its maximum altitude in the course of these events: 37,924 feet. The angle of attack was 18.3 degrees and for the first time the aircraft started losing altitude. Basically, the nose was up and the engines were on maximum power but it was coming down gently and from an aerodynamic point of view this was logical because the aircraft was totally outside its performance envelope.

02:11:10.9 (Synthetic voice): *STALL!*

02:11:11.5 (Synthetic voice): *STALL!*

02:11:12.3 (Synthetic voice): *STALL + cricket!*

02:11:13.7 (Synthetic voice): *STALL!*

02:11:14.3 (Synthetic voice): *STALL!*

02:11:15.1 (Synthetic voice + cricket): *STALL!*

For many long seconds the two First Officers tried to understand what was happening but they remained totally silent. Not a word… David R did not touch his joystick while Pierre-Cédric B kept his almost always in the backward position. When from time to time he let go, the pitch attitude and the angle of attack decreased at once… proof that all that was needed was basic flying to return to normal. But these "dive" movements were short-lived and were immediately countered by brutal pull-ups. The incidence continued to waver between 10 and 18 degrees. For things to have got better it should not have been allowed to exceed 4 degrees.

So the stall alarm continued to sound in the cockpit:

02:11:16.5 (Synthetic voice): *STALL!*

02:11:17.2 (Synthetic voice): *STALL!*

As the Captain had still not turned up, David R sounded the Flight Rest chimes again.

02:11:17.9 (Synthetic voice + cricket): *STALL!*

Then suddenly two series of short, very dull sounds could be heard. This was the aircraft shuddering as it hit against the streams of air coming from the wings and began to vibrate. This was an aerodynamic phenomenon characteristic of stalling. How could they still not grasp what was happening? Apart from the stall alarm which had sounded for the 23rd time, this violent jarring noise should have told the First Officers what was going on.

02:11:19.3 (Synthetic voice): *STALL!*

02:11:20 (Synthetic voice): *STALL!*

Neither man made the slightest comment to show he had understood what was going on. Up until now, nobody had used the word "Stall". Neither of them had said anything about the synthetic voice which had been piercing their eardrums for the last minute and a half.

As the Captain had still not appeared, David R pressed the High-Low Chime button again, which chimed inside the couchette. Meanwhile the alarm sounded with renewed vigour!

02:11:20.7 (Synthetic voice): *STALL!*

02:11:21.4 (Synthetic voice): *STALL!*

02:11:21.4 (First Officer David R): *We've put the thrust on! What the fuck's going on?*

One cannot help feeling that David R reacted rather better than Pierre-Cédric B. His failure to adapt probably resulted from the fact that he did not have the stick in his hands. If he had been aware that his colleague was constantly pulling the nose of the aircraft up, he would no doubt have reacted differently.

02:11:22.8 (Synthetic voice): *STALL!*

02:11:23.5 (Synthetic voice): *STALL + Cricket!*

This time, the angle of attack reached 29.9°. This is unimaginable for an airliner. Maybe the Tupolev in the previous account reached such a figure before going off into its fatal spin.
During the first moments of the tragedy the sink rate was moderate but was now reaching 6,800 feet per minute. And this speed was increasing with every second. However, although the situation was serious, it was still retrievable. All that was needed was a simple movement of pushing the stick forwards and waiting with no further sudden movements. The aircraft would have accelerated then stabilised. The First Officer could even have done something simpler and more decisive in *just letting go of the controls*. The Airbus was at 38,000 feet and the surface of the Atlantic was more than 7 miles under its wings. Despite all the shaking the First Officer had given it, the airplane had already proved it was not going to go off into a spin. Getting out of the stall would surely require a certain amount of time but there was still a big margin. They could come out at about 25,000 feet and everything would return to normal again[53]. The one thing that had to be avoided was to pull the joystick right back.

2:11:24.6 (First Officer David R): *I don't understand what's going on.*

---

[53] The author has checked this out in an Airbus 330 simulator. With identically unfavourable figures the aircraft ends up stabilising itself.

02:11:24.6 (Synthetic voice): *STALL!*

Suddenly between two stall alarms, a woman's voice echoed in the cockpit.

02:11:24.9 (Hostess): *Stephanie!*

No doubt the hostess was worried by the aircraft's movements and wanted to know what was going on. Then the interphone was cut off and the stall warning continued its terrible litany.

02:11:26.3 (Synthetic voice): *STALL! + Cricket.*

02:11:27.7 (Synthetic voice): *STALL!*

02:11:28.4 (Synthetic voice): *STALL!*

02:11:29.1 (Synthetic voice): *STALL! + Cricket.*

02:11:30.5 (Synthetic voice): *STALL!*

02:11:31.2 (Synthetic voice): *STALL!*

02:11:31.9 (Synthetic voice): *STALL! + Cricket[54].*

The Airbus passed 36,500 ft with an increasing sink rate. At that moment the indicated airspeed fluctuated between 128 and 164 knots[55]. For that altitude, this was incredibly low and the control surfaces seemed not to be reacting. Below is the information as it appeared on the Primary Flight Display.

02:11:32.6 (First Officer Pierre-Cédric B): *Fucking hell, I'm not in control of the aircraft!*

02:11:34.7 (First Officer Pierre-Cédric B): *I'm not in control of the aircraft!*

What is even more astounding is that when the First Officer said this he had just pulled the stick back as far as it would go and

---

[54] It would be impossible to include all the stall alarms in the text as some of them occurred at the same time as the First Officers were talking.

[55] 148.12 and 189.37 mph.

to the left. He kept this amazing position for exactly 40 seconds! No aircraft can fly in these conditions without finding itself very quickly in trouble. And the least you could say was that the Airbus was temperamentally very stable! It just remained banked peacefully to the right without putting its nose into the vertical as most other aircraft would have done.

But what is most surprising is that each time Pierre-Cédric let off a bit, the attitude came down again. The only thing the aircraft wanted to do was set off again! All you had to do was stop pulling on the stick!

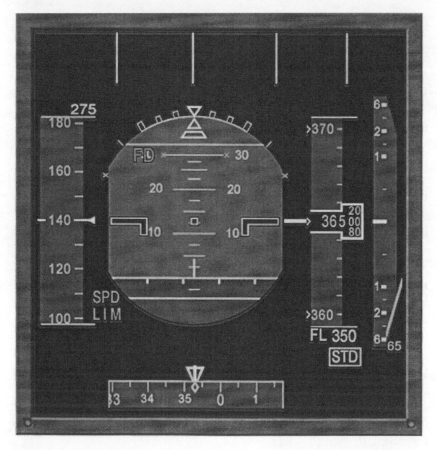

Attitude: 12.5°
Speed: 140 knots
Flight level: 365 (36,500 feet)
Heading: still 049
Variometer: 6,500 feet

02:11:36.1 (Synthetic voice): *STALL!*

02:11:36.7 (Synthetic voice): *STALL!*

David R suddenly seemed to grasp the fact that he could no longer remain a mere spectator and decided to take priority over Pierre-Cédric B's stick. He pressed at length on the red button and then, respecting the procedure, he announced:

02:11:37.5 (First Officer David R): *Controls over to the left!*

Unfortunately, as soon as he had taken over the controls, he too reacted instinctively and instead of pushing the stick forward to reduce the pitch attitude, he pulled the stick right back and to the left, exactly like Pierre-Cédric. He pulled as far as he could, which evidently had no effect. The aircraft remained banked to the right with an angle of attack now beyond 40 degrees.

02:11:38.9 (Synthetic voice): *STALL!*

02:11:39.5 (Synthetic voice): *STALL!*

02:11:40.2 (Synthetic voice): *STALL!* + *Cricket.*

The angle of attack came back down to 33 degrees. The Atlantic Ocean was still seven miles below them.

02:11:41.2 (First Officer David R): *Shit, where are we? What's that, there?*

02:11:41.2 (Synthetic voice): *STALL!*

Then as the stall alarm sounded for the fortieth time, Pierre-Cédric B used words that showed just how unaware he was of what was happening:

02:11:41.2 (First Officer Pierre-Cédric B): *I think we've got a lot of speed there!*

It was evidently only an impression because as the First Officer spoke, the aircraft was flying at 106 knots... just about 122.5

mph[56]. Now, as it was still at 36,038 feet, it was totally outside its performance envelope. The sensation of speed that the First Officer could feel was in fact the result of the aerodynamic noises caused by stalling and the sink rate which continued to increase. The aircraft was falling faster and faster.

It was at this moment that the door opened and the Captain entered the cockpit. Even before sitting down, he asked:

02:11:43 (Captain): *Eh... what the bloody hell do you think you're doing?*

02:11:47.7 (First Officer David R): *What's going on? I don't know what's... I don't know what's going on!*

02:11:44.5 (Synthetic voice): *STALL!*

02:11:45.5 (First Officer Pierre-Cédric R): *We're losing control of the aircraft!*

02:11:46.7 (First Officer David R): *We've lost control of the aircraft. We just don't understand... We've tried everything...*

At the time the Captain entered the cockpit, the parameters were the following:
- Altitude: 35,372 feet
- Speed: 100 knots (115.62 mph)
- Sink rate: about 10,000 feet per minute
- Attitude: 15°
- Angle of attack: 41.5°

Even during flight tests, nobody had ever imagined the aircraft could be put through such acrobatic positions. Remember the stall alarm sounded if the angle of attack was greater than 4°; it was now at 41.5°!

At the very same time as the Captain shut the cockpit door, the stall alarm sounded again. It did so once then became silent as the flight data it sought to insist on were now totally worthless, having nothing to do with normal flight. This was a very rare case of what the manufacturers call NCD, or Non Computed Data. In fact

---

[56] This is the Conventional Airspeed indicated on the Primary Flight Display.

the parameters of this type of flight have never been researched during tests or even on a simulator as the instruments are simply not designed for such a situation. An aircraft cannot fly beyond a certain incidence. Over those limits, the information supplied to the computer has no significance and even the best computers cannot make use of it. A Pitot probe, for example, cannot give any information on the speed if the aircraft descends flat because the airstreams remain tangent to the tube and cannot enter it. Likewise the aircraft reversing is also an unlikely case of NCD. In reality, the airplane was too far outside its performance envelope for the computer to supply coherent information.

We shall return to the stall alarm being temporarily interrupted. At first the interruption only lasted eight seconds but this gave rise to a fierce debate among the crew that lasted much longer.

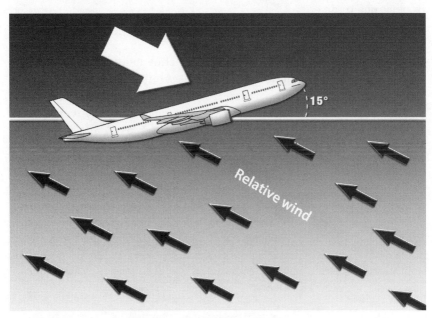

Although the engines were at full power, the airspeed was only 100 knots.

Due to the stall alarm going silent, the cockpit's acoustic environment changed completely. The other alarms became operative again and it was the C-Chord that took over. Its whistle meant that the altitude selected for cruising was not being respected[57].

---

[57] From now, each time the stall alarm stopped because the data were invalid, it was replaced by the C-Chord alarm signalling that the programmed altitude was not being respected.

The Airbus was now at 35,372 feet.

The Captain had just closed the cockpit door but he behaved unexpectedly. He simply folded down the central jump seat[58] and sat down. It is hard to understand this reaction since it was quite clear that things were going wrong on his aircraft. Both First Officers had just told him that they had lost control. David R had even exaggerated by saying they had "tried everything". It was an extremely serious situation and Marc D, who was ultimately responsible for the flight, had enough experience to understand this. It would have been normal for him to order one of them to hand over his seat regardless of whether it was right or left as long as he could take over the controls. In these conditions there is no procedure to define which First Officer should relinquish his position even though logic would require the one with the least experience to do so.

However, Marc D chose to sit down in front of the central console between his two First Officers.

When writing this book, the present author asked some Captains (some of them working for Air France) what their reaction would have been on finding that their First Officers had lost control of the aircraft. Their unanimous response was that they would have chucked one of the First Officers out and got stuck in. Some even admitted that they way they about this would have been energetic to say the least.

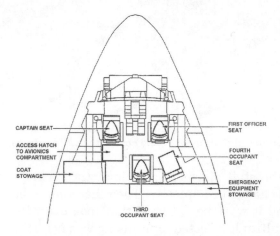

The seats occupied on the flight deck

---

[58] The Airbus 330 cockpit includes two jump seats located on the right hand partitions behind the First Officer's seat.

In an emergency situation, a Captain's role is certainly not to sit on a jump seat and watch his subordinates struggle to control an airplane whose reactions they fail to understand. In the present case it was a question of life and death but even then it was not too late to redress the situation. The aircraft was at 31,000 ft. Even though the sink rate had reached 14,800 ft/min, there was still time to recover and every time Pierre-Cédric B released his stick slightly, the aircraft reacted and its pitch attitude decreased. It could still recover.

02:11:50.5 (First Officer David R): *Er...*

02:11:52.6 (Captain): *Now take that!*

It is not clear to what parameter he was referring. The BEA investigators thought it was the FPV[59] which showed the general trend of the aircraft's flight path.

Then, 0.2 seconds later, the data became valid again. The angle of attack decreased to 41 degrees and the calculator was no longer "NCD". From that instant the stall alarm started again.

02:11:52.8 (Synthetic voice): *STALL!*

02:11:53.4 (Synthetic voice): *STALL!*

02:11:54.2 (Synthetic voice): *STALL + Cricket !*

02:11:55 (Captain): *Now take that one!*

The problem had started two minutes earlier and the situation was surprising to say the least: the Pitot probes had temporarily iced over but were now working again and the crew was struggling with another problem that no longer had anything to do with the original issue.

02:11:55.5 (Synthetic voice): *STALL!*

---

[59] Flight Path Vector, found on the primary Flight Display Screen. The Airbus Manual calls it the "Bird" (and also the Velocity Vector on other types of aircraft). The FPV designates the place where the aircraft will be in a few seconds if the controls remain in same position.

02:11:55.7 (Synthetic voice): *STALL!*

02:11:56.3 (Synthetic voice): *STALL!*

02:11:57 (Captain): *Try and take that…*

From now on, the Non Computed Data situation occurred intermittently. The indications on the screens alternated between valid and non-valid when the angle of attack was above or below 41 degrees or when the First Officer pulled on his stick or let go of it.

02:11:58.2 (First Officer Pierre-Cédric B): *The problem is that I haven't got any vario there[60].*

02:12:01 (Captain): *Okay.*

02:12:02.5 (First Officer David R): *We haven't got a single valid reading!!*

Here, once again, Pierre-Cédric B became distraught. As just a few seconds earlier, he now imagined the aircraft was in overspeed whereas in reality the aircraft was with difficulty moving at 90 knots[61], barely the speed of a Cessna 152 training aircraft.

02:12:04.3 (First Officer Pierre-Cédric): *I get the impression this is a completely crazy speed, isn't it? What do you think?*

Once again David R made a better analysis of the situation.

02:12:06.6 (First Officer David R): *No!*

However, Pierre-Cédric B took no heed of this and proceeded to make another mistake, again reacting according to his confused physical impressions. This is precisely what you should avoid doing when flying without any outside references and when only the instruments count. Because he *felt* the Airbus was flying at tremendous speed, the First Officer applied the speed brakes at a time when the aircraft was already at much too low a speed! David R reacted at once:

---

[60] The variometer measures the vertical speed of the aircraft (see the right-hand scale on the PFD diagram).
[61] 104.3 mph.

02:12:07.2 (First Officer David R): *No, don't put the airbrakes on!*

At the time the speed brakes were applied the aircraft was at 29,736 feet. The ocean was still 6.12 miles beneath the aeroplane and recovery remained a possibility although time was now short as the sink rate had increased again having reached more than 15,300 feet per minute. This was enormous – more than 20 times the normal rate of descent for a commercial aircraft during an approach. Every spilt second would now count.

Putting the speed brakes on had brought no response from the Captain and only David R had reacted decisively. Persuaded by his colleague's reaction Pierre-Cédric retracted the speed brakes.

02:12:07.7 (First Officer Pierre-Cédric B): *No? Okay...*

02:12:07.7 (Synthetic voice): *STALL!*

02:12:08.3 (Synthetic voice): *STALL!*

02:12:09 (Synthetic voice): *STALL!*

02:12:10 (Synthetic voice): *STALL!*

02:12:10.6 (Synthetic voice): *STALL!*

The aircraft continued to plummet at great vertical speed, going down flat with its wings fluttering. The angle of attack was 40.4 degrees. And surprisingly, neither First Officer knew who had priority on the stick. In fact, they did not know who was flying the aircraft. So, although priority on the joystick was still on the left, David R shouted:

02:12:12.9 (First Officer David R): *Pull!*

Apart from the fact that he should have said "push", the First Officer did not realise that he was in fact the one who was in a position to do something. They were both in a situation of intense stress that incapacitated them.

Meanwhile, the Captain seemed strangely absent.

02:12:14.4 (First Officer David R): *What do you think? What do you think? What should we do?*

02:12:15.5 (Captain): *Well, dunno. It's going down.*

Such an admission of helplessness was tragic. Here too, it is hard to understand why the Captain did not just ask for his seat back. Marc D had just stated that the aircraft was going down at top speed. His First Officers had admitted several times that they were no longer in control of the aircraft but the Captain still remained strangely passive. He could have got angry with them, or even insulted them, but instead of this he merely issued a few mild words of advice. Was he tired or was it a problem of circadian rhythm? In his defence, you have to remember that he had only just returned to the cockpit a minute earlier and that his First Officers had not given him the slightest explanation as to what had happened while he had been absent.
We shall probably never know why the Captain took no initiative. This was all the more incomprehensible since the aircraft was still at 25,000 feet, just two minutes before the point of no return...

Then suddenly, the synthetic voice resounded in the speakers with a new message:

02:12:17 (Synthetic voice): *Priority on the right!*

Pierre-Cédric B had just pushed the red button on the stick to again take over the controls (contrary to procedure, he did not announce he was going to make this move).
Unfortunately this new change of pilot had no effect. The former cadet had no sooner got hold of the stick than he pulled it at once right back just as before. So the Airbus continued to fall in the position forced upon it from the outset with its nose up and an attitude fluctuating between 7 and 13 degrees. This pitch was characteristic of a certain form of stalling. Under the First Officer's control, the nose of the aircraft went up and down producing movements much like a dolphin jumping up and down in and out of the water. In such conditions it was a wonder the aircraft did not just tip over onto one wing and go off into a steep turn. The airplane was in fact incredibly "healthy" from an aerodynamic point of view.

02:12:19.6 (First Officer Pierre-Cédric B): *There we are.*

02:12:20 (Synthetic voice): *STALL!*

02:12:20.8 (First Officer Pierre-Cédric B): *There we are. The wings are back on the level, aren't they?*

From the outset, the First Officer had focused on the wings having to be level. At no point did he seem to realise that this was not the most important parameter. How could he have continued to persist in ignoring the synthetic voice screaming the word "stall" in his ears? The real issue was not to level the wings but to stop blocking the aircraft's attitude and let the nose go down below the horizon. Nothing else really counted.
At that moment, the angle of attack reached 43.5 degrees!
As the Captain did not have the stick in his hands, he remained unaware that his First Officer was holding his right against his guts. All his attention was focused on the wings too:

02:12:23 (Captain): *Level the wings... the horizon... the standby horizon.*

02:12:25.5 (First Officer Pierre-Cédric B): *The standby horizon...*

02:12:26.6 (First Officer Pierre-Cédric B): *The speed...*

02:12:27.4 (First Officer David R): *You're climbing!*

The aircraft was certainly not climbing but falling ever faster but the First Officer was taken in by its nose-up attitude.

02:12:27.2 (Synthetic voice): *STALL!*

02:12:27.4 (Synthetic voice): *STALL!*

02:12:28.1 (Synthetic voice): *STALL!*

02:12:28.3 (First Officer David R): *You're going down... Down... Down...*

02:12:30.0 (First Officer Pierre-Cédric B): *Am I going down now?*

02:12:31.8 (First Officer David R): *Go down!*

02:12:32.4 (Captain): *No, you're climbing!*

02:12:32.8 (First Officer): *I'm climbing up there? Okay. So we're going down…*

The atmosphere in the cockpit was now turning to panic. The words "up" and "down" were repeated in quick succession without any indication that there was any real understanding of what was going on. Even the Captain, as a passive spectator, seemed totally disconnected from what was happening.

02:12:34 (Synthetic voice): *STALL!*

02:12:35 (Synthetic voice): *STALL!*

Then suddenly, for some unknown reason, Pierre-Cédric B pushed his stick forward…The aircraft reacted immediately. The nose descended onto the horizon and the pitch came back down to 8 degrees, then to -2 degrees. For a short while, it even went down to -7 degrees. With both General Electric engines delivering their maximum thrust (68 tons under the wings) there was a real chance of pulling out and stabilising the situation[62]. All they had to do was continue to push gently on the joystick to recover. The speed had been almost zero but was starting to increase.

Unfortunately the Airbus is not a four-seat aircraft and it takes time to get its 200 tons going again. However, the First Officer only held that position on the controls for 7 seconds and this was nowhere near enough to recover from the stall. It remains hard to understand what precisely was going on in their heads except that as soon as the flight data had improved, Pierre-Cédric B returned to his catastrophic knee-jerk reaction of pulling back on his joystick. So the vicious circle recommenced and the more he pulled back the more the aircraft fell.

02:12:39.2 (First Officer Pierre-Cédric B): *Okay. We're on TOGA…*

02:12:40.2 (Synthetic voice): *STALL!*

02:12:40.5 (Synthetic voice): *STALL!*

02:12:41.2 (First Officer Pierre-Cédric B): *What are we on there? What are we on there?*

---

[62] Each General Electric CF6-80-E1A3 delivers 73,530 lb or 34.3 tons of thrust.

The First Officer was interrupted by two dull cracking noises.

The Airbus had started buffeting again and the airstreams were coming unstuck under the effect of the angle of attack which had again started to rise. The aircraft was trembling violently.

02:12:42.4 (Synthetic voice): *STALL!*

02:12:43.2 (Synthetic voice): *STALL!*

The altitude was now 20,028 feet, the engines were still at full power, the sink rate was about 15,000 feet per minute and the airspeed was between 127 and 153 knots[63].
The Captain still remained out of it.

02:12:43.8 (Captain): *Shit, it isn't possible!*

02:12:44.7 (First Officer Pierre-Cédric B): *What's our altitude?*

Strangely the question seemed to surprise David R who asked at once:

02:12:47.5 (First Officer David R): *What do you mean altitude?*

No answer...

02:12:46.2 (Synthetic voice): *STALL!*

02:12:48.9 (First Officer Pierre-Cédric B): *Yeah... yeah... yeah. I'm going down there, am I?*

02:12:48.9 (Synthetic voice): *STALL!*

02:12:50.3 (First Officer): *Yes, there, you're going down! Yes!*

02:12:51.8 (Synthetic voice): *STALL!*

02:12:52.3 (Captain): *There, you... you're...*

The Captain then immediately clarified this vague comment:

02:12:54.5 (Captain): *Level out the wings.*

---

[63] 176.87 and 14.87 mph.

02:12:56 (First Officer David R): *Level out the wings.*

02:12:56 (First Officer Pierre-Cédric B): *That's what I'm trying to do.*

02:12:57.2 (Captain): *Level out the wings!*

The stall continued to destabilise the Airbus which was banking continually from one wing to the other. Every time the aircraft banked to one side, Pierre-Cédric B would pull the stick right back in the opposite direction. All instructors will tell their trainees that this is the last thing to do. When you are high-angle flying, it is essential to move the ailerons as little as possible because this will produce exactly the reverse effect. Pushing the stick to the right increases the right bank.

Understandably, the man complained that the control surfaces were ineffective but still failed to realise that levelling the wings was not the priority.

02:12:58.6 (First Officer Pierre-Cédric B): *I'm full aileron.*

Only now did the Captain grasp what was happening. Was the experience he had gained flying lighter machines at last beginning to pay off?

02:12:58.6 (Captain): *The rudder!*

This was sound advice... To master an airplane with a high angle of attack when it is banking you have to use the rudder and avoid deflecting the ailerons (which latter movement always turns out to be counter-productive). Even if, as in the present instance, the Airbus was not at all tending to go into a spin, you still need to control it with your feet.
Why the Captain did not order the First Officer to reduce the pitch attitude remains a matter for speculation. In reality, he probably did not realise how fiercely Pierre-Cédric B was clutching and pulling back on his joystick.
The best way to proceed would have been for the Captain to take his seat. Unfortunately he did not do so.

02:13:05.9 (Captain): *Wings level... go on... gently... gently...*

02:13:11 (First Officer David R): *We've lost everything on banking.*

02:13:11.3 (Captain): *Okay...*

02:13:14.4 (First Officer David R): *I haven't got anything there!*

02:13:14.8 (Captain): *What... you've got what... No, wait.*

The reason David R got no response from the ailerons was that Pierre-Cedric had again taken priority over the controls away from him.
For a few seconds now, the stall alarm had stopped sounding... All data were again invalid and this time the interruption lasted for 57 seconds. As before, it was replaced by the C-Chord alarm warning that the aircraft was not maintaining its altitude.
This was precisely what was worrying Pierre-Cédric B because the Airbus was now at less than 12,000 feet.
The ocean was now only 2.37 miles below the aircraft.

02:13:18 (First Officer Pierre-Cédric B): *We're there... we're there... we're passing level 100!*

It was then that David R suddenly understood that he did not have priority on the joystick and that he was not in control anything. He reacted at once:

02:13:19 (First Officer David R): *Wait... Me, I've got the controls... I've got the controls, haven't I, eh?*

There was another instance of "rivalry" over the commands. From this moment onwards, David R held down the red button to assert his takeover. The synthetic voice clearly pronounced the words "dual input" in the speakers. This meant that both pilots had control of the mini-stick but it was only the algebraic sum of each move that would be passed on to the control surfaces. The result was that the Airbus continued falling towards the Atlantic at a vertiginous sink rate. Little by little, its heading curved towards the right and it started a wide turn to the south.

02:13:25.3 (First Officer Pierre-Cédric B): *What... How come we're going down so fast there?*

02:13:28.2 (First Officer David R): *Try and see what you can do with your controls up there! The primaries, etc.*

Once again these remarks show that the First Officers had still not grasped the fact that they were in a stall situation. David R had just suggested Pierre-Cédric B go over to "Direct" Law control. Unfortunately, this could only make things worse. It was precisely because the aircraft had been on Alternate Law that it had not gone off into a spin. The guardian angel was still there and, although discreetly, continued to do the job.
The altitude was now 10,092 feet.
The ocean was getting nearer... the die now seemed to have been cast. Even if the sidesticks had at last been pushed fully forward, it would probably have been well-nigh impossible for the aircraft to recover.

02:13:31.7 (First Officer Pierre-Cédric B): *We're reaching level 100 ...*

02:13:36.5 (First Officer Pierre-Cédric B): *9,000 feet!*

Sitting between the two First Officers, the Captain still did not understand what was happening. As Pierre-Cédric was now making violent motions with his feet, he tried to calm him down:

02:13:38.6 (Captain): *Gently does it with the rudder, there!*

02:13:39.7 (First Officer David R): *Climb... climb... Climb... Climb...*

02:13:40.6 (First Officer Pierre-Cédric B): *But I've been pulling full backward on the stick since earlier.*

With this stunning comment, the First Officer had just pathetically summed up what had been wrong since the beginning of the incident with him just pulling back almost unrelentingly on the stick. In these circumstances the Airbus could never return to its performance envelope.
This time, hearing his First Officer say that he had been pulling back on the stick for all his might, the Captain seemed to react, seeming finally to have understood.

02:13:42.7 (Captain): *No, no, no… don't go up, no. No.*

02:13:43.5 (First Officer David R): *So, go down…*

But as the controls were still on "dual input" with each pilot negating the input from the other, David R ended saying:

02:13:45 (First Officer David R): *Give me the controls… me the controls!*

02:13:46 (First Officer Pierre-Cédric B): *Go on… you've got the controls… We're still on TOGA, aren't we?*

If the Airbus had still been at a high enough altitude, one could say that this was the turning point of the tragedy: ever since the beginning Pierre-Cédric had remained stubborn: "I'm pulling on the stick… it doesn't work but I'm the one who's flying the aircraft". It was only now that the end was nigh that he finally consented to hand over the controls to David R. Unfortunately, it was too late. The Airbus was at less than 6,000 feet and falling just as quickly. As soon as David R took over the joystick, the parameters once more became valid and the stall alarm started again:

02:13:55.4 (Synthetic voice): *STALL!*

02:13:56 (Synthetic voice): *STALL!*

02:13:56.7 (Synthetic voice): *STALL + Cricket !*

02:14:05.3 (Captain): *Careful, you're pulling!*

02:14:06.5 (First Officer David R): *I'm pulling?*

02:14:06.5 (Captain): *You're pulling!*

02:14:07.3 (First Officer Pierre-Cédric B): *We're nose-up, we're at 4,000 feet!*

02:14:10.8 (Captain): *You're pulling there!*

As Pierre-Cédric B had just announced, the Airbus was at 4,024 feet. At that moment, the data were as follows: speed was between

60 and... 30 knots[64]. This was incredibly low. Despite the engines being pushed to their limits, the sink rate was around 10,000 feet per minute. Pitch attitude had decreased to around 12 degrees but now that Pierre-Cédric had handed over the controls it descended to −4 degrees in a nose down dive.

It was now too late to do anything. The angle of attack was still a staggering: 42.5° but the Airbus no longer had enough altitude leeway to come out of the stall. A new alarm sounded. This time it was the GPWS which had just detected the ocean... The water was getting nearer at full speed. The synthetic voice cried out that the sink rate was too high... Pull up... Pull up...

02:14:18 (Captain): *Go on, pull up!*

Altitude: 2,140 feet...

02:14:19.2 (First Officer David R): *Go on... Go on pull up... pull up... pull up!*

There was no way out. If the crew continued to pull on the stick as the First Officer had been doing, the aircraft would continue to pursue its infernal high-angled fall and end up hitting the ocean in a belly flop. If, on the other hand, the First Officer pushed down on the stick as he should have done from the very beginning, the attitude would decrease but they would still hit the water in a dive. Either way, the result was going to be a crash.

At that moment, Pierre-Cédric B decided to take over the controls again. Once again he did not warn his colleague who continued to pilot the aircraft without realising that his joystick had become inactive again. In the last seconds of the flight, the mini-sticks were in their original positions, revealing what had been happening ever since the beginning of the tragedy:

- David R's stick was positioned very slightly forwards and it was probably at this time that the First Officer really understood things and wanted to gather speed. Even if his chances were nil, his reaction here was the right one.
- Pierre-Cédric B's stick was positioned in the full backward position, as it had been for most of this hellish descent. He had still not understood.

---

[64] Between 69.37 and... 35 mph.

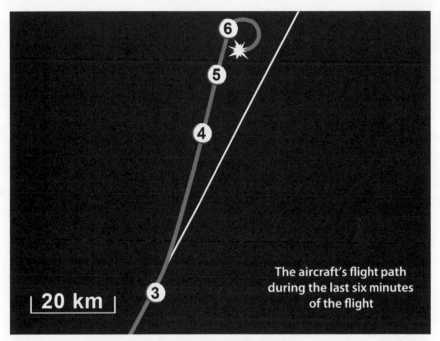

The aircraft's flight path
during the last six minutes
of the flight

20 km

The final flight path of the Airbus as a 2D diagram based on the French civil aviation accident investigation agency (BEA) report

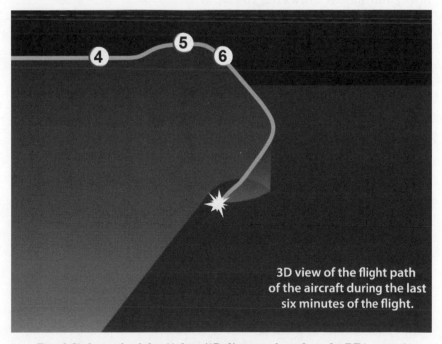

3D view of the flight path
of the aircraft during the last
six minutes of the flight.

Final flight path of the Airbus (3D diagram based on the BEA report)

Their very last words were indicative of each man's state of mind:

02:14:23.7 (First Officer David R): *Shit. We're going to crash... It's not true!!*

02:14:25.8 (First Officer Pierre-Cédric B): *But what's going on?*

One of them had probably understood while the other remained in complete ignorance.

Then as the GPWS voice warned them to pull up, it was the Captain who spoke the last words:

02:14:26.8 (Captain): *Attitude 10 degrees...*

The Airbus hit the Atlantic Ocean near Point "TASIL". At the moment of impact, its speed in relation to the sea was just 107 knots (124 mph). Despite its engines running at full power, its sink rate of 10,912 feet per minute was enormous. As can be seen from this diagram, it was on a magnetic heading of 270, which means it had done more than a half circle during its fall and its nose was now pointing back towards Brazil.

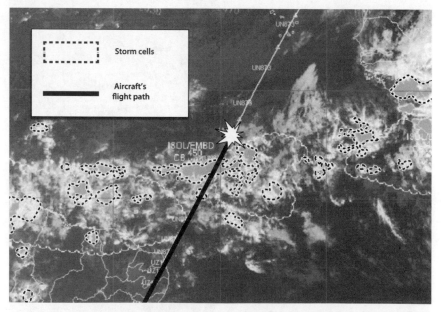

This photo was taken about an hour before the accident. It shows that the area of the crash was beyond the danger zone

The stall lasted exactly 4 minutes and 24 seconds during which the synthetic voice pronounced the word "stall" 75 times.
In accumulated time the alarm had sounded for 54 seconds.
The recording stopped at **02:14:28.2** as the aircraft broke up on impact and the occupants were killed outright.

TWO YEARS' SILENCE

For almost two years the world speculated as to what actually happened to flight AF 447. Surprisingly, the Air France Communications Manager put forward the idea that the Airbus could have been struck by lightning and had just disintegrated in flight at high altitude... The pilot of the Air Comet 974 flight[65] confirmed that he saw a white light in the night as he was crossing the ITF. The specialists however remained wary of this highly fanciful theory.
The possibility of the Pitot probes icing over was put forward as an explanation. This theory was supported by hard facts based on a historical record of probes that had already broken down in the past and the knowledge that at the outset of the tragedy the Airbus had sent off automatic ACARS messages indicating that the airspeed indicators were malfunctioning.
So the anemometric probes were suspected as being the cause of the crash.
However, proof was lacking and, as time went by, the hope of finding the wreck diminished. The search zone was enormous and the depths concerned were considerable. But the investigators remained determined. Five different search campaigns were conducted in the South Atlantic[66] and considerable financial resources were devoted to the undertaking. Finally and quite unexpectedly the wreck was localised on 4 April 2011. This was a tremendous technical feat since the localisation transmitters had stopped working long ago.

On 1 and 2 May 2011, the two flight recorders were brought to the surface. They were in good condition and their data were perfectly legible. The inquiry's next stage was then supervised by the investigation agencies from four different countries (France, Brazil,

---

[65] Here again it was an Airbus 330-200 that was flying the Lima-Madrid route and whose flight path was close to that of AF 447.
[66] See le mystere du vol rio-paris by Roger Rapaport, published by Editions Altipresse.

Germany and Great Britain) and to avoid any later controversy the recordings were opened and listened to in the presence of police investigators.

THE CONTROVERSY SURROUNDING THE PITOT TUBES

Analysis of the DFDR and CVR[67] parameters confirmed that the anemometric probes ceased functioning at 02 hours 10 minutes. This was most likely due to icing-up but the phenomenon was short-lived and could not in itself have been the cause of the crash. This was just a contributory factor, as was the sudden increase in temperature and the cumulonimbi. Some people objected that if the probes had not iced over, the autopilot would not have been disconnected and the pilots would therefore not have lost control of the aircraft. This view is rather restrictive since if the incident had taken place in daytime and in fine weather, there would not have been an accident in the first place. Besides, this was not the first time an Airbus 330 (or 340) had lost its speed indications or suffered other such anomalies. Indeed, the BEA has drawn up an inventory of reports from crews who had experienced the same type of problem:
- 4 cases with Air France.
- 2 cases with the Brazilian airline TAM.
- 4 cases with Qatar Airways.
- 1 case with Air Caraïbes.
When these events occurred there was a temporary interruption of the speed displayed on the screens, strangely similar to what happened on AF 447 as they occurred at high altitude (above level 340), in very stormy weather, by night or in clouds. Above all, each interruption had been preceded by an abrupt rise in the outside temperature accompanied by more or less heavy turbulence.
In all events, the autopilot was disconnected and the Airbus went over to "Alternate" law. But in all cases, the crews applied the appropriate procedure and the aircraft remained within its flight envelope after which everything returned to normal and the aircraft reached its destination in complete safety.

---

[67] Digital Flight Data Recorder and Cockpit Voice Recorder.

THE CONSPIRACY THEORY

The BEA published its interim report N° 3 on 29 July 2011[68]. Publication of this document naturally led to an outcry from Air France, its main pilots' union and the victims' families. There was talk of a "farce", of "blue-pencilled" reports... It was a conspiracy intended to protect French aeronautical interests by blaming the pilots for the tragedy. Even the periodic silence of the "stall" alarm was put forward as an explanation for why the crew failed to realise what was happening.

The furore reached paroxysmal proportions when it was learnt that the BEA had withdrawn a "project of recommendations concerning the functioning of the stall alarm". The integrity of the agency was unfairly called into question. Its directors did all they possibly could to explain that these recommendations were premature at this stage of the investigations, but to no avail: the harm was done. In a press release, Alain Bouillard, in charge of the inquiry, explained "that ever since (I) started this job, (I) have never been subjected to the slightest pressure." This was a man to be trusted with a true reputation for unswerving integrity, but withdrawing the recommendations nevertheless made the newspaper headlines. To put paid to this senseless speculation, the French Minister of Transport logically explained that "if we had wanted to hide the truth, we would not have organized search campaigns and spent 35 million Euros". It is true that the South Atlantic Ocean is vast and all they needed to do was to keep looking in the wrong direction for the crash of Flight AF447 to remain an enigma forever.

It is time to stop acting as hypocrites. It would appear that there are some countries where the pilots never make mistakes and, when an accident occurs, it is always caused by external factors - the evidence is systematically denied. Recently a pilot even committed suicide at the controls of his aircraft with all the passengers aboard and the immediate reaction of the airline executives was to assert that the man concerned was 100% fit to fly.

And then there are more advanced countries where the parameters are examined objectively and investigators seek to understand what part the human factor paid in the tragedy. Corporatism, national pride or commercial interests have no part to play in the information to be published. If there were pilot errors, then they are revealed for all so that they can be used as useful "feedback" to

---

[68] The technical parameters used in this book are mainly taken from this report available at the BEA site on http://www.bea.aero/fr/enquetes/vol.af.447/vol.af.447.php.

serve other pilots. Until evidence to the contrary, this is one of the best ways to improve on air safety and make progress. The United States are in the lead in this domain. Everything is transparent and even Russia is making real progress...

It remains to be seen where we stand in France.

PRONOUNCING THE WORD "STALL"

The truth here is that during the 4 minutes 24 seconds between the beginning and the end of the tragedy, the word "stall" was never once uttered by a crew member. The investigators believe the three men had no real grasp of the reality of the situation. Despite the alarms, the buffeting, the drop in speed, the loss of altitude, nobody understood what was happening.

On any other type of aircraft the tragedy would have ensued much more rapidly. At that altitude, a Tupolev would have tipped over onto one wing, gone into overspeed and most certainly disintegrated in flight. The problem was that the Airbus is an incredibly "sturdy" aircraft (if this was not the case, the dozens of pilots using it would have said so long ago). Even though it went onto "Alternate" law, the computer prevented it from tipping over and the descent was incredibly long. Unfortunately the three man crew was unable to take advantage of this reprieve.

HAS THIS TYPE OF ACCIDENT ALREADY OCCURRED?

The answer is YES!

Although stalling is a manoeuvre all trainee pilots learn about during their training, this was certainly not the first time an aircraft had crashed due to incorrect piloting.

- On 22 December 1996 at Greenboro, North California, a DC-8 from Airborne Express was carrying out a test flight after maintenance tests. The trials were carried out at a height of 15,000 feet. The aircraft stalled but at no moment did the crew stop pulling back on the stick. The aircraft plummeted to the ground[69].

- On 12 February 2009, a DHC-8 from Colgan Air was on its approach to Buffalo, N.Y. The Captain did not understand that his aircraft was on the point of stalling. He resisted and the aircraft plunged into a steep turn.

---

[69] In le secret des boites noires by the same author, published by Altipresse.

- Not to forget the accident of the MD 80 of West Caribbean on 16 August 2005[70] following which Martinique went into mourning. The conditions of this crash were incredibly similar to those of AF 447: a night flight, above a cumulonimbus, near the ITF, with a heavy aircraft and a Captain insisting on pulling the stick back until impact. The problem with the Pitot tubes can in no way explain away the tragedy that occurred on Flight AF 477. All aircraft have failures in flights. However, procedures exist to overcome such situations and are to be applied rigorously. Uncontrolled reactions and poor reflexes have no place here. The stark reality is that the First Officer in the right-hand seat made a beginner's mistake.

But the real question will be to determine who or what was responsible for all this waste and determine a strategy in response. Was it a problem of training, tiredness, circadian rhythm, or simply the result of the pilots being lulled into believing that an Airbus can make up for absolutely all their mistakes?

It will be up to the investigators to explain how qualified pilots could act that way. Whatever happens, the Rio-Paris crash still caused 228 victims and the families deserve to be told the full truth of the matter...

---

[70] In Erreurs de pilotage Vol 2 by the same author, published by Altipresse

SUMMARY

Editions JPO

FROM FLIGHT SCHOOL TO THE A380

by *Claude Lelaie*

Young pilots landing their single engine airplane imagine themselves doing the same thing from the left seat of an A380.

Is it as easy?

The answer is yes… with a few small differences due the aircraft's inertia, and to the fact that the pilot sits more than 30 feet above the ground before initiating the flare.

On the other hand, an airliner's take off procedures are different from a light plane's because an engine failure must, on no account, lead to an accident. With safety as a common thread, from flying to flight preparation, from training to aircraft design.

Claude Lelaie is a qualified engineer with a distinguished career as test pilot, fighter pilot and airline pilot, during which he has clocked up more than 16,000 flying hours, including 9,000 in testing. He joined Airbus in 1988 where he was from 1994 Head of Flight Tests and then Head of Product Safety.
He was pilot-in-command on the first flights of both the A340-600 and the A380.
Claude Lelaie lives in Toulouse, France.

Visit our website

WWW.editions-jpo.com

find us

on facebook *and* twitter

Imprimé en France. - JOUVE, 1, rue du Docteur Sauvé, 53100 MAYENNE
N° 2696493G - Dépôt légal : février 2018